[redacted]

Rinaldo and Armida

Recent Researches in Music

A-R Editions publishes seven series of critical editions, spanning the history of Western music, American music, and oral traditions.

Recent Researches in the Music of the Middle Ages and Early Renaissance
Charles M. Atkinson, general editor

Recent Researches in the Music of the Renaissance
James Haar, general editor

Recent Researches in the Music of the Baroque Era
Steven Saunders, general editor

Recent Researches in the Music of the Classical Era
Neal Zaslaw, general editor

Recent Researches in the Music of the Nineteenth and Early Twentieth Centuries
Rufus Hallmark, general editor

Recent Researches in American Music
John M. Graziano, general editor

Recent Researches in the Oral Traditions of Music
Philip V. Bohlman, general editor

Each edition in *Recent Researches* is devoted to works by a single composer or to a single genre. The content is chosen for its high quality and historical importance and is edited according to the scholarly standards that govern the making of all reliable editions.

For information on establishing a standing order to any of our series, or for editorial guidelines on submitting proposals, please contact:

A-R Editions, Inc.
Middleton, Wisconsin

800 736-0070 (North American book orders)
608 836-9000 (phone)
608 831-8200 (fax)
http://www.areditions.com

Recent Researches in the Music of the Baroque Era, 176

John Eccles

Rinaldo and Armida

Edited by Steven Plank

A-R Editions, Inc.
Middleton, Wisconsin

The Works of John Eccles
Michael Burden, Amanda Eubanks Winkler, Alan Howard,
Kathryn Lowerre, *General Editors*
Anthony Rooley, *Honorary Editorial Board Member*
Olive Baldwin, Thelma Wilson, *Research Associates*

Performance parts are available from the publisher.

A-R Editions, Inc., Middleton, Wisconsin
© 2011 by A-R Editions, Inc.

All rights reserved. No part of this book may be reproduced or transmitted in any form by any electronic or mechanical means (including photocopying, recording, or information storage and retrieval) without permission in writing from the publisher.

The purchase of this edition does not convey the right to perform it in public, nor to make a recording of it for any purpose. Such permission must be obtained in advance from the publisher.

A-R Editions is pleased to support scholars and performers in their use of *Recent Researches* material for study or performance. Subscribers to any of the *Recent Researches* series, as well as patrons of subscribing institutions, are invited to apply for information about our "Copyright Sharing Policy."

Printed in the United States of America

ISBN 978-0-89579-723-0
ISSN 0484-0828

♾ The paper used in this publication meets the minimum requirements of the American National Standard for Information Sciences—Permanence of Paper for Printed Library Materials, ANSI Z39.48-1992.

Contents

Abbreviations and Sigla vii

Foreword, *Anthony Rooley* viii

Preface, *Michael Burden, Amanda Eubanks Winkler, Alan Howard, and Kathryn Lowerre* ix

- Eccles's Life and Career ix
- Editing Eccles's Works ix
- Notes x

Acknowledgments xi

Introduction xiii

- The Original Production xiii
- The Original Performers xiv
- Synopsis xiv
- The Musical Entertainments xv
- Performance Considerations xvi
- Notes xviii

Plates xxi

Rinaldo and Armida

- Dramatis Personae 2
- Title Page to the Playbook 2
- Dedication to the Playbook 2
- Preface to the Playbook 3
- Preface to *The Musical Entertainments* (1699) 4
- Notes to the Prefatory Materials 4
- Prologue 5
- Act 1 5
  - Musical Entertainment No. 1 6
  - Musical Entertainment No. 2 13
- Act 2 26
  - Musical Entertainment No. 3 29
- Act 3 37
  - Musical Entertainment No. 4 39
- Act 4 61
  - Musical Entertainment No. 5 62
- Act 5 95
  - Air: "Ah Queen" 96
- Epilogue 99

Additional Music from *Rinaldo and Armida*
Country Dance 102
Minuet 103
Rigadon I 104
Rigadon II 105
Passepied I 106
Passepied II 107
Air: "Behold in what glorious condition" 108

Critical Report 109
The Sources 109
Editorial Methods 110
Critical Notes 111

Appendix: Playbook Versions of the Sung Texts in *Rinaldo and Armida* 113

Abbreviations and Sigla

Abbreviations

GMO	*Grove Music Online*, Oxford University Press, http://www.oxfordmusic.com/
MB	Musica Britannica
ODNB	*Oxford Dictionary of National Biography*, Oxford University Press, http://www.oxforddnb.com/
RRMBE	Recent Researches in the Music of the Baroque Era

Library Sigla

GB-Lbl	London, British Library
GB-Lcm	London, Royal College of Music

Foreword

The untimely death of Henry Purcell in 1695 caused a deep sense of loss to be felt not only by his wife and his close friends and colleagues, but also by the wider artistic circle that inhabited London's vibrant theater life. But the show had to go on, so to speak, and the public's voracious appetite for new theater productions demanded a steady stream of music for the stage: instrumental suites, music to accompany onstage action, lively and tuneful songs, mad songs, bold and brazen duets—all forms in which Purcell had excelled. A number of able composers met the demand, including Daniel Purcell and the prolific John Eccles, whose skill in setting a broad range of dramatic lyrics was, even in his own time, legendary.

Such a contemporary reputation has not, however, translated into a modern-day enthusiasm for Eccles's works, thanks to the long shadow cast by Henry Purcell's towering genius. The latter's reputation rests partly on the posthumously published two-volume anthology *Orpheus Britannicus,* a masterpiece of English song filled with a breathtaking variety of mode and mood and covering Purcell's contributions to theater productions from his final decade. Purcell was not alone in publishing a compendium of theater songs: his contemporary John Blow produced a similar publication, *Amphion Anglicus,* which is hardly less thrilling (not to mention that its "Amphion" resonates with Purcell's "Orpheus"). But Eccles's *A Collection of Songs for One, Two, and Three Voices* (published in 1704) has not met with such enduring popularity, at least in modern scholarship, where very few articles even refer to its existence. Perhaps its prosaic title does not sell it so well—but even a cursory glance at its contents reveals that here is the very heart of English theater song.

Welcome, then, to this "collected works" of John Eccles, a man who in his time was the very epitome of dramatic, character-driven theater music. Eccles, a close friend and creative partner of William Congreve (perhaps the most persuasive dramatic writer of that age) and composer of choice for Anne Bracegirdle (the greatest singing actress of the time), here receives the recognition hitherto denied him. His large-scale works reveal a careful architectural planning, a sense of varied pace, a brilliant delineation of the dominant passion, and a superb handling of forward energy unsurpassed even by Purcell. At a fairly casual count, there are over ten masques and operatic works for which Eccles provided the complete stage music and upwards of sixty plays to which he contributed songs, dances, and incidental music together or severally. In addition, Eccles composed numerous court odes (for many of which the music is lost) and contributed to a variety of miscellaneous instrumental contributions and publications. Nearly all of this material is included in the present series.

This endeavor—an example of extended cross-Atlantic teamwork—had its genesis in February 2005 when Jeffery Kite-Powell hosted a conference devoted to the music of Eccles at the College of Music at Florida State University, Tallahassee, where two years before, as "Visiting Orpheus Professor" (Curtis S. Mayes Orpheus Chair in Musicology), I had directed a production of Eccles's *Semele.* Many of the conference participants had previously discussed the possibility of an edition of the complete works of John Eccles; now, with that stimulus and with the detailed bibliographic work of Olive Baldwin and Thelma Wilson as a road map, the project's editorial team has embraced the considerable labors necessary to bring those plans to fruition.

That I am now writing this foreword is proof enough of the editorial team's success. I am a practical man, a performer with "scholarly pretensions" (in that if one wishes to walk the untrodden paths of ancient music one has to develop some library skills and a nose for forgotten gems), and I have been profoundly moved by my meeting with John Eccles's music—always vital, theatrical, and spirited. He deserves closer attention.

Anthony Rooley

Preface

To English theatergoers in late-seventeenth- and early-eighteenth-century London, the music of John Eccles (ca. 1668–1735) would have been both familiar and welcome.[1] His career, like those of Daniel Purcell, John Weldon, and Gottfried Finger, flourished after the death of Henry Purcell in 1695, with some time being spent as house composer at the theater in Lincoln's Inn Fields. These years saw him writing songs, act tunes, and other incidental music for the plays performed there and contributing to the 1701 competition managed by the publisher Jacob Tonson for the best setting of William Congreve's masque, *The Judgment of Paris*. He was as happy at court as he was in the theater, and produced a number of odes, which included extensive instrumental sections, during the reign of Queen Anne. But the audiences of the period favored what was new over what was old, and the popularity of Eccles's music had long since faded by the time of his death in 1735. Nevertheless, his career spans one of the most interesting periods of English musical history, one during which the focus of musical production shifted from the court of the 1670s and 1680s to the increasingly mercantile, concert- and opera-sponsoring London of the eighteenth century. At the same time, English composition absorbed elements of both French and Italian music, including overture and dance forms from the former and aspects of harmony, texture, and sequential patterning from the latter.[2] These were elements with which London audiences had a conflicted relationship: on the one hand they desired them as fashionable and exotic, but on the other they were suspicious of things that were not "English." Eccles himself had absorbed all these influences but was also capable of writing a good "English" tune, a flexibility that placed him in a powerful position in the theater world and made his works among the most popular of the late 1690s.

Eccles's Life and Career

Little is known about Eccles's early life. Born around 1668, we hear nothing of him until the 1690s, for it appears that Eccles, unlike many other English composers, did not begin his career as a chorister in the Chapel Royal. In 1694 he is recorded as a musician (probably a violinist) in the King's Band, although he did not receive a salary until 1696, when he took over Thomas Tollett's duties as one of the king's twenty-four musicians-in-ordinary.[3] From 1700 he was Master of the King's Musick, having replaced Nicholas Staggins, and became the only composer to serve as Master of the King's Musick under four monarchs: William III, Anne, George I, and George II. Presumably because these court appointments rarely paid well (or promptly, or sometimes at all), Eccles devoted most of his energy during this early period of his career to writing for the stage. His theatrical compositions were first published in 1691, and in 1693 he began working for the United Company at Drury Lane. When the United Company split in 1694, Eccles followed the rebel actors—Thomas Betterton, Elizabeth Barry, and Anne Bracegirdle—to Lincoln's Inn Fields. After the theater companies reunited in 1705, Eccles continued to write for the theater, but he must have felt keen disappointment when his ambitious 1707 opera *Semele* (possibly intended for the opening of the Queen's Theatre in the Haymarket) was never performed. In the wake of this debacle, Eccles effectively retired from composition, save for the occasional court ode and, as theater payment records suggest, occasional sets of act tunes and other pieces.[4]

Eccles's theater music, the masques, dramatick operas, and songs and instrumental music for spoken plays,[5] forms the core of his output. While some of the incidental music, such as that for *The Italian Husband*, is somewhat generic, other pieces, such as the symphony for act 2 of *Macbeth*[6] with its serpent and tremolo figures, deserve a place alongside those of Matthew Locke and Henry Purcell.

Editing Eccles's Works

Many of Eccles's works survive in a patchwork fashion due to contemporary compositional and publishing practices. Overtures and act tunes were often composed, printed, and published separately from the songs for a production, while dances appeared in yet other collections. Solo songs and duets were often printed as single sheets in musical periodicals or in songbooks organized by composer or production. Among the printed sources, only John Eccles's own *Collection of Songs for One, Two, and Three Voices*, published by subscription in 1704 and sold by the author, carries the weight of his authority.

Few seventeenth-century English composers left large quantities of autograph material, but Eccles's hand is particularly poorly represented even by this standard. Nevertheless, Richard Platt has identified the surviving score of *Semele* (GB-Lcm 183) as autograph not only on the basis of its numerous compositional revisions but also by comparison to a letter from Eccles to a court official.[7] Other sources that may be autograph are GB-Lbl Add. Ms. 12219 (Eccles's music for *Macbeth*) and GB-Lbl Add. Ms. 31456 (the ode "Inspire us genius of the day").[8] Another manuscript that shares some notational characteristics with GB-Lcm 183 is GB-Lbl Add. Ms. 29378, the most significant source of Eccles's theater music. But whether it is in fact autograph or was produced by an amanuensis working under close supervision, its purpose is clear: it brings together copies, in score, of Eccles's music for major theatrical works from around 1700, including *Europe's Revels for the Peace* and *Rinaldo and Armida* together with many additional songs and some choruses.

With the publication of these volumes, all of Eccles's extant music will be available in modern critical editions (see table 1). In cases where Eccles was a major musical contributor to a dramatic work but did not write all of the music, the surviving contributions of his contemporaries have been included in order to present as far as possible the complete work rather than a fragmentary version. For the dramatic works, the songs and instrumental interludes are given in the order in which they appear in the play, masque, or dramatick opera. Full texts of the masques and the dramatick opera *Rinaldo and Armida* are reproduced, interpolated with the music for each. For the incidental music, plot summaries of the plays are given along with relevant dialogue cues. The remaining works are grouped by genre and arranged in chronological order.

TABLE 1

The Works of John Eccles

Editions	Volume Nos.*
Masques and Operas	
The Rape of Europa, The Loves of Mars and Venus, Acis and Galatea	
Europe's Revels for the Peace	
Rinaldo and Armida	176
The Judgment of Paris	
Semele	MB 76
Incidental Music	
Plays (A–F)	
Plays (H–P)	
Macbeth	133
Plays (R–Z)	
Other Works	
Catches and Drinking Songs	
New Year's Odes and Coronation Music	
Birthday Odes, Cantatas, Hymn to Harmony, and Instrumental Music	

*Series is RRMBE unless otherwise indicated. Those volumes still in progress are listed without volume number.

Michael Burden
Amanda Eubanks Winkler
Alan Howard
Kathryn Lowerre

Notes

1. For an overview of Eccles's career, see Stoddard Lincoln, "John Eccles: The Last of a Tradition" (Ph.D. diss., University of Oxford, 1963). More recently, Kathryn Lowerre has considered his compositions for Lincoln's Inn Fields in *Music and Musicians on the London Stage, 1695–1705* (Farnham, England: Ashgate Publishing, 2009).

2. On the period to circa 1690, see Peter Holman, *Four and Twenty Fiddlers: The Violin at the English Court, 1540–1690* (Oxford: Clarendon Press, 1993), 282–304, 331–58, 413–35. All other recent studies charting this stylistic trajectory have concentrated primarily on Henry Purcell: see, for example, Martin Adams, *Henry Purcell: The Origins and Development of His Musical Style* (Cambridge: Cambridge University Press, 1995), 3–86; Peter Holman, ed., *Henry Purcell* (Oxford: Oxford University Press, 1994), 32–37, 192–200; and Peter Holman, "Purcell's Orchestra," *The Musical Times* 137, no. 1835 (January 1996): 17–23. For a useful summary of genres and forms of instrumental and vocal music associated with the theater in Eccles's lifetime, see Lowerre, *Music and Musicians*, 18–26 and 68–81.

3. *ODNB*, s.v. "Eccles, John (*c.* 1668–1735)," by David J. Golby.

4. Curtis Price, introduction to *Instrumental Music for London Theatres, 1690–1699: Royal College of Music, London, MS 1172*, Music for London Entertainment 1660–1800, ser. A, vol. 3 (Withyham: Richard MacNutt, 1987), vii n. 3.

5. Kathryn Lowerre, "Dramatick Opera and Theatrical Reform: Dennis's *Rinaldo and Armida* and Motteux's *The Island Princess*," *Theatre Notebook* 59 (2005): 23–40. See also the introduction to the present volume.

6. Amanda Eubanks Winkler, ed., *Music for "Macbeth,"* RRMBE, vol. 133 (Middleton, Wis.: A-R Editions, 2004), 7–8.

7. John Eccles, *Semele*, ed. Richard Platt, MB, vol. 76 (London: Stainer and Bell, 2000), xxvi.

8. On GB-Lbl Add. Ms. 12219, see Winkler, ed., *Music for "Macbeth,"* viii. Images from GB-Lbl Add. Ms. 31456 are posted as examples of Eccles's hand in the image gallery maintained by Répertoire International des Sources Musicales (RISM) United Kingdom and Ireland (https://picasaweb.google.com/musicmss/), s.v. "John Eccles." Estelle Murphy has studied the various layers of corrections in GB-Lbl Add. Ms. 31456 in "A King for Europe, a Queen for Britain: Creative Authority in the Birthday Ode for Queen Anne" (paper presented at the Annual Conference of the Society for Musicology in Ireland, University of Ulster, Magee Campus, Derry, Northern Ireland, 7–9 May 2010). Murphy's research forms part of her ongoing work on her doctoral thesis, "The Changing Role of Music at the Stuart Court in the Reign of Queen Anne" (Ph.D. diss., University College Cork, in progress).

Acknowledgments

The general editors would like to thank individuals and institutions that have contributed substantially to the edition as a whole. These include Anthony Rooley, who developed the idea for the project and sketched the first outline of its parameters; Olive Baldwin and Thelma Wilson for their work on sources; Paul Ranzini, who encouraged the original proposal for this series; and Jeffery Kite-Powell, who sponsored the conference "John Eccles and His World" at Florida State University, Tallahassee, in February 2005, which helped to jump-start the project. Tackling a multi-volume work such as this would have been impossible without the collections and the helpful staff of The British Library, the Bodleian Library, Magdalene College, Durham Cathedral Library, The Fitzwilliam Museum, the Folger Shakespeare Library, Yale University Library, Edinburgh University Library, and Chetham's Library.

Michael Burden
Amanda Eubanks Winkler
Alan Howard
Kathryn Lowerre

In the course of preparing this edition I have accumulated a number of debts of gratitude. In particular, libraries that have provided sources and scholarly hospitality, as well as, in a few cases, permission to reproduce material, include The British Library, the Bodleian Library, Durham Cathedral Library, the Library of Congress, the Cleveland Public Library, the University of Michigan Library, Ohio State University Library, and the Oberlin College Library. I am grateful to Amanda Eubanks Winkler, Kathryn Lowerre, Michael Burden, and Alan Howard for their keen editorial oversight and to Olive Baldwin and Thelma Wilson for their generous assistance in navigating source material. I am grateful as well to the entire staff of A-R Editions for their careful review of the work-in-progress and their many suggestions that helped to shape the final product. To Ryan Welsh I owe particularly strong gratitude for his excellent work as digital amanuensis. I am also grateful to Oberlin College for a Research and Development Grant-in-Aid in support of this project. This edition is the work of recent years, but I am mindful that it also had a formative beginning in a musicology seminar at Washington University in 1976 under the mentorship of Sir Curtis Price; for his enthusiastic introduction to *Rinaldo and Armida* and his inspiring tutelage, my gratitude is both deep and long-lived.

Steven Plank

Introduction

Like many musical works for the seventeenth-century stage, the dramatick opera *Rinaldo and Armida* by John Dennis and John Eccles survives in a number of partial sources, a state that reflects both the fluidity of the material and a contemporaneous awareness of the marketability of that material to various categories of consumers, ranging from theater enthusiasts to amateur musicians. Sources with a direct connection to the original production of the dramatick opera include the printed play text and a separately printed text of the musical entertainments in the play, the latter being especially valuable for its descriptive cues and an introductory essay by Dennis. The musical materials include a nearly complete manuscript score (GB-Lbl Add. Ms. 29378) and two printed anthologies (John Eccles's *A Collection of Songs for One, Two, and Three Voices Together* and his *Theatre Musick*) that provide one of the airs and some of the dance music from the production. The musical content of Restoration theatrical productions was often fluid; thus, a printed song sheet from 1699 gives another air ("Behold in what glorious condition") associated with the performance but not found in either of the text sources. And two songs ("Ah Queen" and "The jolly breeze") exist in multiple sources, pointing to their marketability and also providing a measure of their relative popularity. However, this range of source material cannot allow us to recover the complete work: act tunes, stage music, and two stanzas of vocal music at the end of the second act are lost.

The Original Production

The tragedy *Rinaldo and Armida* by John Dennis with "Musical Entertainments" by John Eccles was performed at the Lincoln's Inn Fields Theatre in 1698, most likely in November or early December.[1] The resident company at Lincoln's Inn Fields was a troupe that had split from the United Company, the company created by the merger of the King's Company (housed at the Theatre Royal in Drury Lane) and the Duke's Company (at Dorset Garden Theatre) that had held a firm grip on the London stage from 1682 to 1694. Led by the actors Thomas Betterton, Elizabeth Barry, and Anne Bracegirdle, the breakaway company in its first years operated democratically, with the actors sharing control of the enterprise. Those who did not break away from the United Company stayed at Drury Lane as the Patent Company under the leadership of Christopher Rich. This establishment of two competing companies in the 1690s was, not surprisingly, a spur to dramatic competition and ambitious projects. Even so, the "operatic" performance of *Rinaldo and Armida* by Betterton's company was unexpected at Lincoln's Inn Fields. Although it had been renovated in 1695, the theater remained relatively small—it was known pejoratively as "Betterton's Booth"[2]—and its size imposed considerable constraints upon the spectacular effects that in part defined "dramatick operas" like *Rinaldo and Armida.*

Dramatick opera was in 1698 the reigning form of English musical theater. Its hybrid structure combined spoken drama with masque-like musical scenes, the latter gratifying a lingering taste for the pre-Commonwealth court entertainments that in the new political contexts of the Restoration moved to a safer home in the public theater. Emerging in the 1660s with such productions as Sir William Davenant's version of *Macbeth* with Betterton in the title role, dramatick opera came into full bloom in the early 1690s with works including *The Prophetess, The Fairy Queen,* and *King Arthur,* all set by Henry Purcell and also involving Betterton.[3] Thus, in staging *Rinaldo and Armida,* Betterton would have known firsthand both the expense and the audience appeal of such endeavors.

An anonymously published *Comparison between the Two Stages* (1702) offers a description of *Rinaldo and Armida* that confirms both the novelty of the venue and the widespread interest the production generated:

> *Critick:* At last, (as you say) the old Stagers moulded a piece of Pastry work of their own, and made a kind of Lenten Feast with their *Rinaldo* and *Armida;* this surpiz'd not only *Drury-lane,* but indeed all the Town, no body ever dreaming of an *Opera* there; 'tis true they had heard of *Homer's* Iliads in a Nut-shel, and Jack in a Box, and what not? But where's the wonder? Why such amazement? I have seen the Creation of the World, *Alexander's* Exploits, *Robin Hood* and *Little John,* and I don't know how much, all epitomiz'd into a Rarre-show, carry'd about on a Man's Head. Nay, a certain Bard . . . tells us of a famous Mathematician who drew the whole World on a Cherry-stone; nay, did it so gingerly, that every Country might be seen upon't as plain as St. *Pauls* in the great Map of *London.*
>
> *Sullen:* Well, with this Vagary they tug'd a while, and *The Jolly—Jolly breeze—came whistling thro'*—all the Town, and not a Fop but ran to see the *Celebrated Virgin* [undoubtedly Anne Bracegirdle] in a Machine; there she shin'd in a full Zodiack, the brightest Constellation there.[4]

The interest in the production—"not a Fop but ran"—suggests the strong contemporary appeal of operatic productions.[5] *Rinaldo and Armida* may indeed have gained the attention of the town, but it was an attention that could not be sustained. In response to the opera by the actors' cooperative, Rich's company at Drury Lane offered one of its own: Peter Anthony Motteux's *The Island Princess* with music by Daniel Purcell, Richard Leveridge, and Jeremiah Clarke, a production with which *Rinaldo and Armida* could not compete.[6] Once again, *A Comparison between the Two Stages* offers a telling description:

> *Sullen:* The *old House* have a Bawble offer'd 'em, made out of *Fletcher's Island Princess,* sometime after alter'd by Mr. *Tate,* and now erected into an Opera by *Motteux:* The Actors labour at this like so many Galley Slaves at an Oar, they call in the Fiddle, the Voice, the Painter, and the Carpenter to help 'em; and what either the Poet nor the Player cou'd do, the Mechanick must do for him. . . . [T]he *Opera* now possesses the Stage, and after a hard struggle, at length it prevail'd, and something more than Charges came in every Night: The Quality, who are always Lovers of good Musick, flock hither, and by almost a total revolt from the other *House* [Lincoln's Inn Fields], give this new Life, and set it in some eminency above the *New;* this was a sad mortification to the old Stagers in *Lincolns-Inn-fields.*[7]

Clearly the "bawble" of *The Island Princess* gleamed brightly, casting a shadow on the once-appealing luster of *Rinaldo and Armida.*

The Original Performers

The original playbook lists the principal speaking characters and the actors[8] who played them:

Rinaldo—Mr. Betterton
Ubaldo—Mr. Thurman
Carlo—Mr. Scudamore
Armida—Mrs. Barry
Urania—Mrs. Bo[w]man
Phenissa—Mrs. Lee

In his sixties at the time of *Rinaldo and Armida,* Thomas Betterton (Rinaldo) was decades into the long career that had seen him emerge as the leading actor of his generation and a guiding managerial force in the London theater. His own work had been shaped by William Davenant, who first engaged Betterton as an actor in the Duke's Company in 1661 and assigned the younger actor the wide range of roles that would characterize his career as a whole. Davenant's death in 1668 led to Betterton's long tenure as co-manager of the company, first with fellow actor Henry Harris and later with William Smith. It was under this management that the new theater at Dorset Garden was built and the cultivation of spectacular operatic productions blossomed. Betterton and Smith continued to manage the United Company from its formation in 1682 until 1687; with the creation of the actors' cooperative company at Lincoln's Inn Fields in 1695, Betterton's managerial acumen was again brought into play. When in 1705 the Lincoln's Inn Fields company moved to the new Queen's Theatre in the Haymarket, Betterton resigned the management to William Congreve and John Vanbrugh but continued to act there until his death in 1710.

Predictably, Betterton's leading lady in *Rinaldo and Armida* was the great actress of the day, Elizabeth Barry (Armida)—a pairing of unquestioned prominence, and by this time a familiar one. Barry, like Betterton, had been nurtured by Davenant, but she had also received guidance from John Wilmot, Earl of Rochester, her sometime lover. Her range of roles, like Betterton's, was wide, and she was known for her impassioned renditions, a bent that contrasted well with the virginal persona of her fellow actress Anne Bracegirdle. Bracegirdle, who had been brought up in the Betterton household, achieved great prominence as a singing actress in both the United Company and the breakaway company at Lincoln's Inn Fields, where she was strongly associated with the music of Eccles. Although she is not named among the performers of *Rinaldo and Armida,* she is undoubtedly the "Celebrated Virgin" cited in *A Comparison between the Two Stages,* possibly singing the role of Venus.[9] Bracegirdle was not the only "adopted daughter" in the Betterton household: Elizabeth Bowman (née Watson) (Urania) was another beneficiary of their generosity, and like Bracegirdle, she figured prominently in Betterton productions. In 1692 she married John Bowman, the singing actor prominently associated with the role of Grimbald in Purcell's *King Arthur* and with the famous air "Let the dreadful engines" in part 1 of Purcell's *Comical History of Don Quixote.* Although there is no direct evidence that John Bowman himself participated in *Rinaldo and Armida,* it is likely that he sang the impressive music of the Spirit in acts 1 and 4.[10] Barnabas Scudamore (Carlo) was a member of the United Company by 1694 and followed Betterton to Lincoln's Inn Fields, appearing there in a number of works, including *She Ventures, and He Wins; The City Bride; Rule a Wife, and Have a Wife; The City Lady;* and *The Mourning Bride.*

Two additional singers in the production can be identified through concordant printed sources. Mr. Gouge is named as the singer of the air "Ah Queen" in both of its sources and of "The jolly breeze" in three sources.[11] Gouge was active at Lincoln's Inn Fields during 1698–99 and perhaps afterward as well. He was both a composer and a singer, with several songs appearing in the periodical *Mercurius Musicus.* The printed song sheet versions of "Ah Queen" and "The jolly breeze" appear in treble clef, but the use of bass clef for "The jolly breeze" in GB-Lbl Add. Ms. 29378 suggests that Gouge was a baritone. Mrs. Hodgson is identified as the singer of the air "Behold in what glorious condition" in its only source.[12] Mary Hodgson, the daughter of dancing master Benjamin Dyer and the wife of actor John Hodgson, sang "If love's a sweet passion" in Purcell's *The Fairy Queen* and was praised for her performance as Juno in Eccles's *The Judgment of Paris.*

Synopsis

Prologue. The author rationalizes the liberties he has taken with Tasso's characterizations of Rinaldo and

Armida. With regard to Armida, "here you see no soft bewitching dame," but rather a "proud, fierce, stormy, terribly severe" heroine, worthy of the tragic muse. On the other hand, the heroic refashioning of Rinaldo is necessary because in the Italian his manners are "unequal found."

Act 1. Urania, Ubaldo, and Carlo, allies of the Christian hero Rinaldo, encounter a paradisiacal scene, the place where Rinaldo spends his days in the embraces of the enchantress Armida and his "luxurious nights in wanton joys." Urania commissions Ubaldo and Carlo to free the hero from this captivity, for the freedom of captive Jerusalem depends on his participation. The would-be rescuers, in turn, hear enchanting harmonies and are subjected to the allurements of spirits in the guise of shepherds and nymphs. Carlo and Ubaldo, however, resist this temptation, and Urania praises them for gaining this victory over themselves.

Act 2. Inside her enchanted palace, Armida is disquieted by the fear that she will lose Rinaldo, who, though captive himself, has obviously captured her heart. She realizes that even her occult powers cannot calm the "homebred furies which rebel" in her "wild ungovernable mind." Motivated by the anxiety of loss, she summons dreams to enslave the soul of Rinaldo, and he is visited by the shapes of his parents, Bertoldo and Sophia, warning him to abandon the pursuit of fame and to love Armida. Rinaldo awakens to ponder his situation; he laments that he has fallen from the path of glory and hopes that Armida might be content to know that she alone had the power so to move his soul. Armida, who has overheard his soliloquy, plans her response—she will subject him to the "charms of pleasure"—but, lest that fail, she also bids the "gloomy gods" of hell to prepare their attack.

Act 3. In the enchanted wilderness, both Rinaldo and Armida experience the hesitation of conflicted emotions. Rinaldo is resolved to follow the path of glory but questions his own ability ever to leave Armida; Armida is ready to throw the powers of hell at Rinaldo but is restrained by her feelings of love. She summons aerial spirits in the shapes of Venus and Cupid to ease the sadness of his soul, but Urania, Carlo, and Ubaldo reappear, and Carlo, newly armed with a sacred wand from Urania, causes the amorous spirits to vanish. Increasingly confounded, Armida bids her minion, Phenissa, to summon "hell's blackest furies."

Subsequently, Rinaldo meets Carlo and Ubaldo, who show him his fallen state and urge him to return to his "godlike self once more." Although conflicted, Rinaldo owns that his love of duty and honor is indeed greater than his love for Armida. Phenissa, learning this, sends Nisroe, another of Armida's minions, to deliver the news destined to turn Armida's love to hate, and, according to her earlier preparations, Armida unleashes her "dreadful power" in response.

Act 4. Armida's tempestuous fury rages against Rinaldo. When they finally meet, he counters her accusation of unfaithfulness by protesting that he will never cease loving her but must nevertheless depart from her. He further asks her to consider her own dishonor in loving one "who vilely could renounce eternal fame." Unable to reconcile him to herself, she angrily raises her dagger in order to slay him; he does not resist but rather bids her strike his breast, wherein she will find her image firmly ensconced. Recognizing the truth of his professions of love, she turns the knife on herself. Rinaldo, in turn, responds with a readiness to take his own life, but Armida stays his hand.

Act 5. Rinaldo rejoices in the discovery that Armida's wound is not fatal, as well as in her renunciation of her occult faith and arts. He seeks to leave her momentarily in order to bring his friends, but Armida sees "winged ill omens" that neither Rinaldo nor Phenissa can perceive. When Rinaldo leaves nonetheless, Phenissa takes the opportunity to work a tragic plot. In order to preserve her own existence, she summons a spirit to bring the false message that Rinaldo has abandoned Armida—he is never again to return. In the resulting state of confusion, Armida kills Phenissa, thinking she has abetted Rinaldo in his betrayal. Perceiving that she has but one true friend remaining—death—Armida again attempts to take her life.This time the wound proves fatal.

Rinaldo, Urania, Ubaldo, and Carlo return to find both the dead Phenissa and the dying Armida. Armida now discovers that it was Phenissa and not Rinaldo who was false, and she dies peacefully with Rinaldo at her side, confident that they will live together in the afterlife. As Urania had earlier explained, Armida's death is heaven's punishment for her impious ways, but the lovers' future reunion is heaven's recompense for her repentance, faith, truth, and constancy.

Epilogue. The author declares that those who have fought with King William against the French, "hunting glory through the dusty field," should view the character of Rinaldo with pleasure, for their own behavior merits greater fame: Rinaldo's renunciation was of "malignant charms," while their sacrifice was of a higher beauty and virtue. Similarly, those women who have been left behind by men following the path of glory should take pleasure in the character of Armida, for they too are favorable in the comparison: Armida impeded the pursuit of glory, while they themselves aided it.

The Musical Entertainments

In contrast to the increasingly Italianate, fully sung drama, the creators of dramatick opera took great care to preserve a rational context for the music, especially as it pertained to which characters sang and on what occasions. Enchanters, shepherds, and the like might sing because it was in their nature to do so: music was an agency for magic, and thus it was rational for incantation to take a musical form on the stage;[13] shepherds dwelled in the lyric pastoral world where song was natural. For heroes, heroines, and ordinary mortals, however, this was not typically the case; thus in *Rinaldo and Armida* neither of the eponymous characters sings a note. As an enchantress herself, Armida would be justified in doing so, but this opportunity was left untouched. Clearly, magical powers did not guarantee a character's musical representation; Armida is not alone among the Restoration sorceresses who did not sing. And in general, the strong conventional boundaries around the music in dramatick opera typically constrained its interaction with the narrative.

In light of this fact, *Rinaldo and Armida* takes on striking critical significance. Dennis's design of the drama and his claims for the music insist on an innovative integrality of the music to the drama, an insistence that was a countervolley against "foreign" (that is, Italian) taste as it was manifest in the theater. Writing about the audiences of the early eighteenth century, Dennis identified three categories of people "who have had no education at all": a "great many younger brothers," those "who made their Fortunes in the late War," and a "considerable number of Foreigners." The foreigners, he notes, favor "Sound and Show, where the business of the Theatre does not require it, and particularly a sort of soft and wanton Musick, which has used the People to a delight which is independent of Reason."[14] Thus it comes as little surprise that in devising *Rinaldo and Armida* with "musical entertainments," Dennis sought a path that would set his tragedy above operas of lower dramatic integrity. When he published separately *The Musical Entertainments in the Tragedy of Rinaldo and Armida* in 1699, he included a preface that delineated his high ideals, writing thus:

> Though the Tragedy of *Rinaldo and Armida*, of which the following Lines are a Part, has gone in the World under the Name of an *Opera;* yet is neither the Dramatical Part of it, like the Drama of our usual *Opera's*, nor the Musical part of it like that which is Sung and Play'd in those Entertainments; For all the Musick in this Play, even the Musick between the Acts, is part of the Tragedy, and for that Reason the Musick is always Pathetick. Now nothing can entertain the Imagination very agreeably but that which moves some Passion, and moves it very much too. . . . [A]nd as nothing can be very Pleasing but what is very Moving, so nothing that is very Moving can be Moving long. . . . I found therefore, that in a Musical Entertainment of length, Variety of Passion, as well as Passion would be absolutely necessary.
>
> In the following Lines [the Entertainments] therefore, I design'd not only to move Passion, but as many Passions as I could successively without doing violence to my subject.[15]

Foremost in Dennis's mind is the dramatic integration of the music; this is in striking contrast to some contemporary operas where the play and the music seem divorced from one another. For Dennis, the music is never gratuitous; it is always part of the dramatic dynamic, always impassioned (in as varied a way as possible), always integral.

The unity of music and drama within the acts is easily perceptible from the nature of the musical scenes themselves. In act 1, music functions both as an agent to summon magic spirits and as a means of seduction by those spirits, who assume the guise of shepherds and shepherdesses. In act 2, a musical setting underscores the lack of reality of the dream figures who appear in the guise of Rinaldo's parents; in act 3, music is a tool of spirits impersonating Venus and Cupid to encourage the reluctant Rinaldo to forsake the path of glory for love; and in act 4, music of great theatricality both inflames and embodies the revenge of Armida's magic spirits. In act 5, the last, a spirit sings once again, this time an air to Armida with the false message that Rinaldo has abandoned her. The words are a lie, but in the music there is no falsehood, only a compelling pathos that makes it inevitable that Armida will believe the message true. And with that tragic belief, she joins her operatic sisters Dido and Arianna in the sisterhood of the abandoned.

Dennis also extends this integrality of music to the instrumental act tunes, and he does so most vividly at the end of act 3. Armida's nascent rage is signaled by serpents and basses playing under the stage, and a dire alarm is played by the instrumental forces. The horrible "dismal blast" of the alarm is shortly afterward repeated as the act tune, powerfully connecting the rage with which act 3 ends and the vengeance with which act 4 begins. It is therefore particularly unfortunate that the act tunes do not survive. Roger Savage compellingly speculates that one reason why Eccles's act music disappeared is that it was too "context-specific"—i.e., the very thing that distinguished it, its dramatic "fit"—may have hindered its more general appeal as part of the published suites.[16]

Clearly the musical scenes further the opera's dramatic goals but at the same time help maintain boundaries of rationality. The frequent association of music with the magical, spiritual, or otherwise "unreal" helps to map out the landscape of the spoken dialogue, safely locating music in contexts where it seems rational to find it. But Dennis's aim at integrality nevertheless shows him to be on the cusp of a "reform of post-Purcellian dramatick opera" and to presage a paradigm of dramatic music that would characterize later operatic aesthetics.[17]

Performance Considerations

Several aspects of the realization of *Rinaldo and Armida* invite comment, especially the constitution of the ensemble, choice of tempos, and ornamental practice. Little of the music is scored for specific instruments; where particular instruments are noted, they are generally for special effect. For example, the score specifies a pair of flutes (recorders) in act 3 to enhance the amorous pastoral setting, and the stage directions in the play refer to serpents and basses playing softly under the stage at the end of act 3 to represent the brewing tempest of Armida's vengeance. In the main, however, the instrumental score has four parts that correspond readily to an orchestra comprised of first violins, second violins, violas, and a basso continuo group. It is clear that the full complement of strings did not always play. In act 4, for instance, several passages are marked "Play all," implying that fewer players accompanied the foregoing vocal solos. By extension, other accompanimental passages, especially those

Example 1. John Eccles, "Ah Queen," measures 1–12, from *A Collection of Songs for One, Two, and Three Voices Together* (London, [1704]) and *Mercurius Musicus: or, The Monthly Collection of New Teaching Songs*, January [1699].

marked "soft," might also be effectively played by reduced forces. Regarding instrumentation of the continuo group, bass violins are given an independent part in several passages in act 4, but the choice of instruments is otherwise unspecified. Harpsichord may best be used selectively: although its presence can be documented in London theaters from the early 1670s,[18] recent scholarship suggests that the harpsichord was largely restricted to the accompaniment of vocal music.[19] Given the contemporaneous popularity of theorbo and guitar, these instruments are strong alternatives for accompaniment in both instrumental and vocal writing.

With regard to tempo, it is important to clarify the conventional associations of time signature and speed. John Playford gives one of the clearest expositions of these relationships in his *Introduction to the Skill of Musick* (whose posthumously published twelfth edition was "corrected and amended" by Purcell). With regard to duple time, Playford/Purcell distinguishes three tiers:

> [T]he first and slowest of all is marked thus **C**: 'Tis measured by a *Semibreve,* which you must divide into four equal Parts. . . . The second sort of *Common-Time* is a little faster, which is known by the *Mood,* having a stroak drawn through it, thus ₵. The third sort of *Common-Time* is quickest of all, and then the *Mood* is retorted thus Ↄ.[20]

In the edition, the distinction between these three meters is preserved by retaining **C** and using $\frac{4}{4}$ and $\frac{2}{2}$ for ₵ and Ↄ, respectively. Triple-meter signatures may appear complex, owing both to a degree of interchangeability and the persistence of what in the late seventeenth century would have been antiquated echoes of mensural proportional notation, echoes whose vestigial significance at the brink of the eighteenth century is difficult to discern, as in Eccles's use of Θ$\frac{3}{1}$ and **C**$\frac{3}{1}$. In the Preface to his *Choice Collection of Lessons* (London, 1696), Henry Purcell outlines a hierarchy of tempo for triple signatures, with $\frac{3}{2}$ very slow, $\frac{3}{1}$ slow, **3** faster, and $\frac{6}{4}$ commonly for "brisk tunes." However, Laurie compellingly notes the general interchangeability of **3** and $\frac{3}{1}$ in Purcell's music for sections with three quarter notes to the bar.[21]

Performers' ornamentation of melodic lines was a touchstone of seventeenth-century style. While the manuscript score offers little indication of specific ornaments, the two concordant sources of the air "Ah Queen" in act 5 point interestingly to the manner in which a singer might decorate a melodic line. The earlier of these (in *Mercurius Musicus,* January 1699) is noticeably plainer, both in its melodic content and in its rhythm. The later version (in *A Collection of Songs,* 1704), by means of the ornamental filling-in of intervals and the frequent use of Lombardic rhythm, transforms the air into a decidedly more interesting song, as illustrated in the example 1. Here the filling in of intervals can be observed in measure 2 and the Lombardic rhythms in measures 4 and 6. All these elements of transformation—the echo of performers' liberties—could be applied to other airs in the work as well.

There are few signs of ornamentation in the manuscript score, although as ornamentation is more generally the province of the performer than the composer and the scribe, this sparseness should not constrain the conventional use of ornaments by singer or instrumentalist alike. Two signs in the manuscript invite clarification. The sign ≠ is most likely a trill indication, although its contemporaneous usage may have been more generalized. And in act 4, to enhance the setting of the text "We shake at the dire confusion we make," the lower choral parts with the word "shake" appear under a wavy line (see plate 3), indicating a tremulous rendering of the notes. This special effect would have been a familiar one from the shivering choruses of Purcell's *King Arthur* and Lully's *Isis.*

With regard to stage effects, the thunder cues in act 4 will inevitably rumble in resonance with the modern association of John Dennis with the idiom "to steal one's thunder." The traditional lineage of the phrase goes back to Dennis's development of a thunder device for his unsuccessful play *Appius and Virginia* (1709) and his agitation at discovering its use by others, causing him to proclaim, "S'death! That is my Thunder" or "They steal my thunder." Reports of exactly what he said, what the device was, and what play he saw vary among sources, the earliest of which are Alexander Pope's *The Dunciad, Variorum* (1729) and John Mottley's "Compleat List of all the English Dramatic Poets . . ." (1747); A. N. Wilkins raises the possibility that the enduring remark may be an invention of Pope's and not an impassioned utterance by a frustrated Dennis.[22] Tellingly, however, a 1709 inventory of theater manager Christopher Rich's "movables" suggests that Dennis may indeed have offered an improvement on the established device of metal balls in a mustard bowl. The inventory, printed in *The Tatler* (16 July 1709) records "a mustard bowl to make Thunder with. Another of a bigger sort, by Mr. D[enn]is's directions, little used."[23] The association of a thunder device with Dennis sets the stage for the famous remark, but the authenticity of its utterance remains uncertain.

Notes

1. William Van Lennep notes that even though the date of the first performance is unknown, advertisements for songs from the play (*The Flying Post: or The Post-Master* [London], 6–8 December 1698) and for the play itself (*London Gazette*, 19–22 December 1698) allow it to be placed not later than early December. Van Lennep, ed., *The London Stage, 1660–1800*, pt. 1: *1660–1700* (Carbondale: Southern Illinois University Press, 1965), 505–6.

2. The prologue to *The Fatal Discovery; or, Love in Ruines* (1698) was "[s]poke by Mr. Powell, in answer to a scurrilous one, spoke against him, at Betterton's Booth in Little-Lincolns-Inn-Fields." Emmett L. Avery and Arthur H. Scouten, introduction to Van Lennep, *London Stage* (intro. repr. as *The London Stage, 1660–1700: A Critical Introduction*, 1968), xliv.

3. Purcell scholar Michael Burden underscores Betterton's formative association with dramatick opera: "Clearly, where Betterton was, dramatick opera was sure to flourish." Burden, "Aspects of Purcell's Operas," in *Henry Purcell's Operas: The Complete Texts*, ed. Michael Burden (New York: Oxford University Press, 2000), 6.

4. Staring B. Wells, ed., *A Comparison between the Two Stages: A Late Restoration Book of the Theatre*, Princeton Studies in English, vol. 26 (Princeton, N.J.: Princeton University Press, 1942), 22; and Van Lennep, *London Stage*, 506. Although *A Comparison* has persistently been attributed to Charles Gildon, doubts to his authorship emerge as early as 1925. See, for example, G. Thorn-Drury, "A Comparison between the Two Stages, . . . 1702," *Review of English Studies* 1 (1925): 96; and Staring B. Wells, "An Eighteenth-Century Attribution," *Journal of English and Germanic Philology* 38 (1939): 233–46.

5. While undeniably popular, dramatick opera was not without its critics. Roger North decried its hybrid nature, observing that "some come for the play and hate the musick, others come onely for the musick and the drama is pennance to them, and scarce any are well reconciled to both." John Wilson, ed., *Roger North on Music: Being a Selection from His Essays Written during the Years c. 1695–1728* (London: Novello, 1959), 307.

6. For a discussion of the competition between the theaters in their early days, see Judith Milhous, *Thomas Betterton and the Management of Lincoln's Inn Fields, 1695–1708* (Carbondale: Southern Illinois University Press, 1979), 129–31. *The Island Princess* has been published in facsimile with an introduction by Curtis A. Price and Robert D. Hume (Tunbridge Wells, Kent: R. Macnutt, 1985).

7. Wells, *Two Stages*, 21–22. See also Van Lennep, *London Stage*, 505.

8. Biographical information follows *ODNB* and Philip H. Highfill, Jr., Kalman A. Burnim, and Edward A. Langhans, *A Biographical Dictionary of Actors, Actresses, Musicians, Dancers, Managers and Other Stage Personnel in London, 1660–1800*, 16 vols. (Carbondale: Southern Illinois University Press, [1973]–93).

9. Kathryn J. Lowerre, "Music in the Productions at London's Lincoln's Inn Fields Theater, 1695–1705" (Ph.D. diss., Duke University, 1997), 383. Lowerre also suggests here that the Cupid to Bracegirdle's Venus was the boy James (Jemmy) Laroche (ca. 1688–1710?). Laroche had sung the role of Cupid earlier in Motteux's *The Loves of Mars and Venus* (Lowerre, "Music," 239; *ODNB*, s.v. "Laroche, James").

10. Lowerre, "Music," 376–77.

11. See sources CS-3, CS-4, and CS-6 in the critical report.

12. "Behold in what glorious condition" was published as "a song in the additions to Rinaldo" (1699), but its text does not appear in Dennis's published versions.

13. I explore this theme in " 'And Now about the Cauldron Sing': Music and the Supernatural on the Restoration Stage," *Early Music* 18 (1990): 393–407.

14. John Dennis, "A Large Account of the Taste in Poetry, and the Causes of the Degeneracy of It" (1702), in *The Critical Works of John Dennis*, pt. 1, *1692–1711*, ed. Edward Niles Hooker (Baltimore: Johns Hopkins Press, 1939), 293.

15. John Dennis, *The Musical Entertainments in the Tragedy of Rinaldo and Armida* (London, 1699); repr. in Luttrell Society, *Theatre Miscellany: Six Pieces Connected with the Seventeenth-Century Stage* (Oxford: B. Blackwell, 1953). The preface is given in full in the present edition.

16. Roger Savage, " 'Even the Music between the Acts . . .': John Dennis, Johann Adolph Scheibe and the Rethinking of Incidental Music, 1698/1738," in *Books and Bibliography: Essays in Commemoration of Don McKenzie*, ed. John Thomson (Wellington: Victoria University Press, 2002), 149.

17. See Kathryn Lowerre's excellent discussion of Dennis and reform in "Dramatick Opera and Theatrical Reform: Dennis's *Rinaldo and Armida* and Motteux's *The Island Princess*," *Theatre Notebook* 59 (2005): 23–40 (quotation from p. 36). For a discussion of this paradigm of dramatic music and Dennis's role in its development, see Savage, "Even the Music," 141–59.

18. Andrew Parrott, "Performing Purcell," in *The Purcell Companion*, ed. Michael Burden (London: Faber and Faber, 1994; repr. Portland: Amadeus Press, 1995), 395.

19. See, for example, Peter Holman's excellent *Four and Twenty Fiddlers: The Violin at the English Court 1540–1690*

(Oxford: Clarendon Press, 1993), 384; and Judith Milhous and Curtis Price, "Harpsichords in the London Theatres, 1697–1715," *Early Music* 18 (1990): 38–46. On the performance of the court violin band without continuo, see Peter Holman, "Purcell's Orchestra," *The Musical Times* 137, no. 1835 (January 1996): 18–19.

20. John Playford, *An Introduction to the Skill of Musick*, 12th ed. (The Savoy [London], 1694), repr. with introduction, glossary, and index by Franklin B. Zimmerman (New York: Da Capo Press, 1972), 75–76. For additional discussion of tempo relationships, see A. Margaret Laurie, "Continuity and Tempo in Purcell's Vocal Works," in *Purcell Studies*, ed. Curtis Price (Cambridge: Cambridge University Press, 1995), 192–206.

21. Laurie, "Continuity and Tempo," 201–2.

22. A. N. Wilkins, "John Dennis' Stolen Thunder," *Notes and Queries*, n.s., 3 (1956): 428.

23. Ibid., 426.

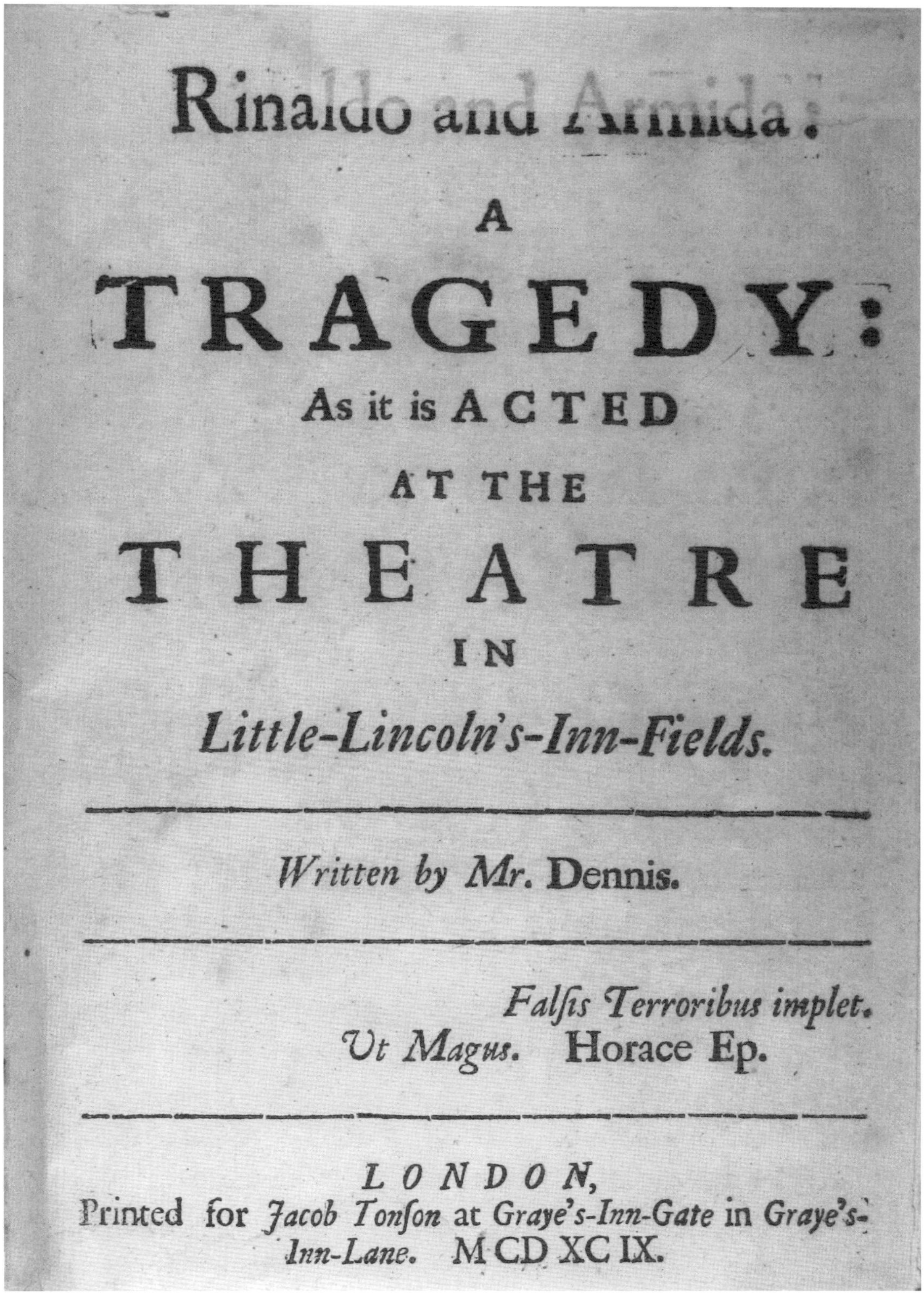

Rinaldo and Armida:

A

TRAGEDY:

As it is ACTED

AT THE

THEATRE

IN

Little-Lincoln's-Inn-Fields.

Written by Mr. Dennis.

Falsis Terroribus implet.
Ut Magus. Horace Ep.

LONDON,
Printed for *Jacob Tonson* at *Graye's-Inn-Gate* in *Graye's-Inn-Lane.* MCDXCIX.

Plate 1. John Dennis, *Rinaldo and Armida: A Tragedy* (London, 1699), title page. Reproduced with permission of the Special Collections Library, University of Michigan.

Plate 2. First page of the manuscript score for John Eccles's musical entertainments in *Rinaldo and Armida* (London, British Library, Add. Ms. 29378, folio 3r.). Reproduced with the permission of the British Library Board. All rights reserved.

Plate 3. A page from the manuscript score for John Eccles's musical entertainment in act 4, measures 210–14 (London, British Library, Add. Ms. 29378, folio 49r).

Plate 4. John Eccles, *Theatre Musick: Being a Collection of the Newest Ayres for the Violin . . . with a Through Bass to Each Dance* (London, [1698]), page 21. Reproduced with the permission of Durham Cathedral.

Rinaldo and Armida

A Tragedy in Five Acts
Written by John Dennis
Music by John Eccles

Dramatis Personae

For the *dramatis personae,* Dennis's playbook lists (after the prologue to the play) only the first six characters and the actors who originally played them (see the introduction), as well as "aerial, terrestrial, and infernal spirits." The lists presented here are editorially created.

Speaking Roles

Armida, an enchantress
Rinaldo, a Christian hero
Ubaldo, an ally to Rinaldo
Urania, the muse of astronomy and an ally to Rinaldo
Carlo, an ally to Rinaldo
Phenissa, a minion of Armida
Nisroe, a minion of Armida
Arioc,[1] a minion of Armida

Singing Roles

Act 1

Spirit (bass)
Nymph (soprano)
Two Shepherds (countertenor and bass)
Trio of Shepherds (SSB)
Chorus of Shepherds and Nymphs (SATB)

Act 2

Sophia (soprano)
Bertoldo (bass)
Chorus of Spirits (SATB)

Act 3

Venus (soprano)
Cupid (soprano)
Chorus of Loves and Graces (SATB)

Act 4

Spirit (bass)
Chorus of Spirits (SATB)

Act 5

Spirit (tenor)

Orchestra

Flute 1, 2
Violin 1, 2
Viola
Basso continuo (including Bass Violins)
Trumpets and Serpent

Title Page to the Playbook

Rinaldo and Armida: | A Tragedy: | As it is acted at the Theater in *Little-Lincoln's-Inn-Fields.* | *Written by Mr.* Dennis. | *Falsis Terroribus implet. Ut Magus.*[2] Horace Ep[istles] | *LONDON,* | Printed for *Jacob Tonson* at *Graye's-Inn-Gate* in *Graye's-* | *Inn-Lane.* M CD [*recte* DC] XC IX.

Dedication to the Playbook

To His Grace, The Duke of Ormond[3]

My Lord,
The world has not been displeased to see in Rinaldo a character resembling your Grace's, a character of a Hero who neither rants nor whines, but is great with a solid and real greatness, very valiant without extravagance, and very human without weakness, and deserting pleasure for glory. And that character naturally claims your protection, which resembling yours has pleased all sorts of people: for your Grace at the same time that you have been the darling of the fair, has been the passion of the brave, and the esteem of the wise. The University of Oxford is proud of such a Chancellor, and the armies of the King of such a Lieutenant General. All who are engaged in the cause of Truth, whether they defend her by force or argument, are animated and excited by having your Grace at the head of them. But at the same time that you have been the darling of the fair and the esteem of the wise, the largeness of your soul and the height of your courage, the love of your country and the love of glory, have made you almost the adoration of the armies. Whenever you were encamped, the old officers beheld with wonder in you a double portion of the greatness of soul of the noble Duke of Ormond, your grandfather. And whenever you were engaged in the field, the old animated soldiers reviewed with ravishment the heroic courage of your father, the brave Earl of Ossory. I must confess, my Lord, the commendation of any man's ancestors is for the most part a superficial and a foreign praise; but to show the high esteem that we have of yours, is to show the value that we have for your Grace. I admire indeed the old noble Duke of Ormond and the brave Earl of Ossory, but I admire them most in your Grace. For the blood of your illustrious family, like the flood of a noble river, becomes more great and more august the farther it descends from its source.

The Earl of Ossory did as much as man could do at Mons,[4] and success attended his actions. Your Grace deserved to be victorious at Landen,[5] but Fortune would not have it so. But 'tis easy, my Lord, to look great in prosperity; to be great in adversity, that is the work. Your Grace in yours appeared so exalted to your enemies that they almost condemned that fortune which had declared for them, and blushed in their captive to behold their superior. I am afraid that I have gone too far, while I have endeavored to please; for to show that I am sensible of your extraordinary merit, cannot but be pleasing to all the world but your Grace. But to show that I had rather have your approbation than that of the world, I here restrain the passion which I have to proceed, and subscribe myself,

My Lord,
Your Grace's most obedient Servant and most humble admirer,
John Dennis

Preface to the Playbook

The Prologue to the play is a sort of preface to it, yet because prose seems to be more adapted to criticism than verse, I desire the reader's leave to say something more largely of things which were mentioned there. I had only the hint of Rinaldo's character from Tasso,[6] but the character is my own. And if anyone objects that by differing from Tasso, I offend in this character against the resemblance of the manners, to him I answer that the manners of Rinaldo in Tasso being unequal, they are consequently not well marked, and that by consequence there can be no character. I was therefore at liberty to form a character from Tasso's hint the most agreeable to my subject that I could.

I designed Rinaldo then neither a languishing nor a brutal hero; he is fond of Armida to the last degree, and yet resolves to leave her, but owes that resolution to the strength of his reason and not the weakness of his passion. And as he resolves to leave her out of sense of his duty and honor, and not any levity or barbarity of nature; so upon their meeting in the fourth act, he demurs upon executing that resolution, neither through fear nor any tender infirmity, but something that happened which seemed to require it from his goodness and his humanity.

For Armida, some gentlemen who have read Tasso may expect to see that wanton, alluring, delicious creature who appears in the fourth canto of the *Gerusalemme,* with all that's tempting in art, but I desire those gentlemen to consider that in that canto she only appears in masquerade and acts a part at the request of her uncle.

Fa manto del vero ala Menzogna,[7] making use of artifices that were contrary to her nature, in order to the seducing the heroes of Godfrey's army. The poet gives her true character in the 38th stanza of the 16th canto of that poem:

> *E cosi pari al sasto hebbe lo sdegno*
> *Ch'amo d'esser amata, odio gli amanti.*[8]

She is by nature a proud and a disdainful beauty: proud of her triumphs, yet disdaining the slaves which adorned them, and so much the more violent in the love she bore to Rinaldo because he was the only person who had touched her soul with tenderness. And therefore I was obliged to show her as the nature of her character and of my subject required. I say not this to arraign Tasso, who is certainly of the greatest of modern poets, but to defend myself, for I leave it to any man of sense to judge whether affectation be becoming of a poem which ought only to express nature or the little arts of a jilt, of the gravity and severity and majesty of the tragic muse.

But now 'tis time to answer an objection. There is, say some gentlemen, a softness that is natural to love, and only that softness, say they, should be capable of engaging Rinaldo's heart, for 'tis hard to conceive, say they, how such a hero should be passionately fond of a woman who appears always either in a furious disorder or using of horrible incantations.

To this I answer that the action of the play begins but between three and four hours before the death of Armida; that before that, the lovers had been three months together in the enchanted island, where she had entertained him with all that is soft and engaging in art and nature; that the fury of her disorder began but an hour before the beginning of the action of the play from a hint which one of her spirits had given her of the approaching danger. All this will appear to the discerning reader from the play itself, who then may perhaps be inclined to believe that I have had a little discretion in my conduct, and that I have taken up the story in that very part of it which alone is proper for tragedy.

The action is very great and important; upon the last event of it depends the success of the most happy and most glorious crusade in which ever the Christians engaged against the infidels. Godfrey's army had beleaguered Jerusalem, which, according to the fable, could not possibly be taken till Rinaldo was returned and had cut down the enchanted grove. As the action is great, the characters are illustrious, and the scene is extraordinary. All the objects that appear to the agents are almost entirely new; every thing they see in nature, being wonderful and surprising; every thing that they see in art, being terrible and astonishing.

I resolved therefore to do my endeavor to treat this subject with something at least of that sublime at once and pathetic air, which reigns in the renowned Sophocles. I resolved to use some effort to make the greatness of the sentiments and of the images answer to the height of the subject, and the dignity of the expression to the greatness of the sentiments. I designed in this poem to make terror the prevailing passion, which is likewise the predominant passion in that admirable Grecian.

The action is not only regular in the mechanism (the incidents falling without any restraint into the narrow compass of the representation), but decent too, I hope, in the conduct of it; and (to the reserve of the machines to which the necessity of the subject obliged me) reasonable.

I have endeavored to show as much address as I could in the management of it. The first act but just opens the design, and just shows Armida in such a light as was likeliest to prepossess an audience in her favor and make them espouse her interests. As soon as I had done that by the mouth of Urania, I thought fit to oblige her to break off the narration, according to the important precept of Horace:

> *Ordinis haec virtus erit et Venus aut ego fallor,*
> *Ut Jam nunc dicat, Jam nunc debentia dici,*
> *Pleraque differat, & praesens in Tempus omittat.*[9]

Armida resumes and continues the narration in the second act, and by displaying the grounds of her jealousy, shows the fundamental qualities of Rinaldo's character and her own: the greatness of her mind, the pride of her soul, the violence of the temper, and the height of her passion, and prepares what she says and does in the fourth act, as Phenissa, by endeavoring in this second act to bring Armida off from her passion, lays the foundation of and prepares the catastrophe.

It may now perhaps be expected that I should say something in the defense of the catastrophe. But the objection against that being almost universal, I should be unpardonably presumptuous if I should imagine that I could be in the right against the consent of so many illustrious assemblies as composed the audiences of this tragedy. All that I shall say in my defense is this: that perhaps I may one day retrench that which displeased them, and that I shall be a little more cautious the next time I am to entertain them.

Preface to *The Musical Entertainments* (1699)

Though the tragedy of *Rinaldo and Armida*, of which the following lines are a part, has gone in the world under the name of an opera, yet is neither the dramatical part of it, like the drama of our usual opera's, nor the musical part of it like that which is sung and played in those entertainments, for all the music in this play, even the music between the acts, is part of the tragedy, and for that reason, the music is always pathetic. Now nothing can entertain the imagination very agreeably but that which moves some passion, and moves it very much, too, for nothing can very much please the fancy, but that which puts the spirits into an extraordinary motion, which extraordinary motion is passion, and for that reason, those who are very old, by reason of the chillness and coldness of their bloods, which, as it were, congeals their spirits, are very rarely or never extremely pleased. The design therefore of music, as well as painting and poetry, being to entertain the imagination agreeably, nothing in music can be extremely fine but what is extremely moving; and experience has confirmed me in this opinion, by so much fine music as I heard in *Italy*, both in their churches and theatres. Now as nothing can be very pleasing but what is very moving, so nothing that is very moving can be moving long. For whether it proceeds from a defect of mind or body, the passions, they are languid, are not delightful, and if they are violent, are not lasting. I found therefore, that in a musical entertainment of length, variety of passion, as well as passion would be absolutely necessary.

In the following lines [the musical texts] therefore, I designed not only to move passion, but as many passions as I could successively, without doing violence to my subject, [such] as admiration, love and joy, anger, compassion, terror, grief, horror, astonishment and despair. How clearly, how fully, and how admirably Mr. Eccles has expressed those passions I leave to the world to judge, which has loudly on this occasion, done justice to his merit, even before the play has been acted. One thing I can say myself, of which I suppose I may be allowed to be a competent judge: that he has everywhere so thoroughly entered into my design, that if I had not known him very well, I should have often wondered at it. I am so much obliged to him for the care and pains which he has taken in this composition, that the least acknowledgment which I can make him is to defend him against the malice of some who have accused him of borrowing a chorus in the fourth act from the Frost Scene [in *King Arthur*] of Mr. Henry Purcell. That great master has been accused himself of borrowing that very music from Lully. I say not this with a design to vindicate Mr. Eccles by recrimination, but only to show that there has been always malice in the world. I have a better way of defending Mr. Eccles, for the chorus which he is pretended to have borrowed from Mr. Purcell is by much inferior to two others in the same entertainment, [viz.] that of the winds and the last. If therefore he has borrowed the worst from Mr. Henry Purcell, I would ask his accusers from whom has he borrowed the best?

Notes to the Prefatory Materials

1. The play text reads "Ariec," but following Milton's *Paradise Lost*, "Arioc" seems most likely intended: "Nor stood unmindful Abdiel to annoy / The Atheist crew, but with redoubl'd blow / Ariel and Arioc, and the violence / Of Ramiel scorch and blasted overthrew" (6.369–72).

2. "Ille per extentum funem mihi posse videtur ire poëta, meum qui pectus inaniter angit irritat, mulcet falsis terroribus implet ut magus: et modo me Thebis, modo ponit Athenis" (That man seems to me able to walk on the tight rope who, as a poet, tortures my breast with fictions, can rouse me, then soothe me, fill me with unreal terrors like a magician, set me down either at Thebes or Athens). Horace, *Epistles* 2.1.210–13; as quoted and translated in *The Routledge Dictionary of Latin Quotations* (New York: Routledge, 2005), 264.

3. James Butler, second Duke of Ormonde (1665–1745). James received the dukedom in 1688, succeeding his grandfather, James (1610–88).

4. Thomas Butler, sixth Earl of Ossory (1634–88), led the English forces fighting in the service of William of Orange and rendered particularly distinctive service at the Siege of Mons in 1678.

5. The Battle of Landen (War of the Grand Alliance), 29 July 1693.

6. That is, Torquato Tasso's *Gerusalemme liberata.*

7. "Vela il soverchio ardir con la vergogna, e fa' manto del vero a la menzogna" (Your overmuch boldness veil with maidenly modesty, and make of the truth a mantle for your lying) Torquato Tasso, *Gerusalemme liberata* 1.25.7–8; translation from idem, *Jerusalem Delivered,* trans. Ralph Nash (Detroit: Wayne State University Press, 1987), 74.

8. "She had a scornfulness so equal to her pride that she loved to be loved but hated those who loved her." Tasso, *Jerusalem Delivered,* 347.

9. "This, or I am mistaken, will constitute the merit and beauty of a just disposition, that the author of the projected poem just now say what ought just now to be said, have the address to put off most of his thoughts, and wa[i]ve them for the present; to embrace one, and reject another." Horace, *De arte poetica,* lines 42–44; translation from *The Works of Horace,* trans. Christopher Smart, 2 vols. (Philadelphia, 1836), 2:385.

Rinaldo and Armida

Prologue

Since what is new, will likeliest entertain you,
With a new Prologue first, we'll strive to gain you.
The Prologue's so entirely new today,
It ne'er can serve for any other play.
Then all you sparks who have to Paris rid,
And there heard Lully's musical Armide;
And ye too, who at home have Tasso read,
This in precaution to you must be said;
Armida's picture we from Tasso drew,
And yet it may resembling seem to few;
For here you see no soft bewitching dame,
Using incentives to the amorous game,
And with affected, meretricious arts,
Secretly sliding into hero's hearts.
That was an error in the Italian muse,
If the great Tasso we're allowed t'accuse;
And to descend to such enervate strains,
The tragic muse with majesty disdains.
The great Torquato's heroine shall appear,
But proud, fierce, stormy, terribly severe,
Such as the Italian has Armida shown,
When by the world's disorder, she'd revenge her own.
To change Rinaldo's manners, we had ground,
Who in the Italian is unequal found.
At first he burns with fierce ambition's fire,
Anon he dotes like any feeble squire,
The mere reverse of all that's noble in desire.
Then in a moment leaves the lovesick dame,
And only burns, and only bleeds for everlasting fame.
In a just play such heroes ne'er have part,
For all that offends nature, offends art.
What we have changed, we leave to you to scan,
Yet judge with all the candor that you can;
So shall your pleasure be the writer's care,
Who for it neither time nor thought will spare;
Which we're not wanting now, to give this play its due,
To make it truly great, and truly worthy you.

Scene: The top of a mountain in the Canaries.

The action of the play begins with the beginning of the Overture, which is a Trumpet Tune, supposed to be played by the good Spirits who have the conduct and care of the action, and the guardianship of the persons concerned in it.

Act 1

Scene: A delightful wilderness on the top of a mountain in the Canaries. Overture with trumpets.

Enter Urania, Ubaldo, and Carlo.

UBALDO: Thus heaven declares th'importance of our enterprise,
While angels their ethereal trumpets sound,
To animate us in our glorious march.

URANIA: At length the labors of that march are o'er,
At length the sharpness of th'ascent is conquered;
And we through ways untractably abrupt
Have reached this towering summit of the mountain,
Where never mortal yet, by mortal force,
Was known t'ascend, from whose commanding height
At once two worlds lie subject to our view.

UBALDO: By its transcendent beauty and its height,
This sure must be the paradise of nature.
O blest retreat! O fields beloved by heaven!
O island justly called the Fortunate,
And with high reason by the ancients thought
Th'Elysian seat of happy heroes' souls!

CARLO: But, O amazing height!
At what remote and what stupendous distance,
Yon tyrannizing main below,
Insults the foaming shore!
Ubaldo, see how very far beneath us
With flagging wings the painted meteors fly
Through all th'infernal regions of the air!
How far below, illustrious in its flight,
The nimble lightning scours along the sky!
And hark how far, how very far beneath us,
Th'exasperated thunder roars,
To plague the guilty world!

URANIA: But never storm disturbs this happy place,
The very pride and pomp of wanton nature,
The very darling of indulgent heaven;
Which still the sun, the world's great eye, contemplates,
And never suffers interposing cloud
To bar th'eternal prospect; 'tis a scene
Not unbecoming of the glorious action,
Which heaven's almighty will has chosen you,
Its ministers t'accomplish; to this place
Armida's magic power conveyed Rinaldo.
Here the great champion of the Christian faith
Lies languishing and half dissolved in love.
The terror of the unbelieving world,
And of thy proud oppressors, O Jerusalem,
Is here become an impious woman's slave!
A woman, who, like Lucifer of old,
Of all the angels of her sex created,
The brightest and the nearest to divinity,
Is fallen and lost by her excessive pride:
And not contented with her native charms,
Holds guilty commerce with infernal spirits.
Here in th'embraces of his young enchantress
The blooming hero passes all his days,
And his luxurious nights in wanton joys,

As wanton as the wings of western winds,
Whose spicy breaths throughout these flowery plains
Maintain eternal spring. Him you must free,
Or thou must still be enthralled, O sacred city;
For on Rinaldo's conquering sword
Thy destiny depends.

CARLO: The very place assists us in the action,
The very place inspires magnanimous thoughts,
As by the help of so sublime a station
Here on the frontiers of the rolling skies,
We stand and breathe, the borderers of heaven;
So exalts our very souls, and lifts them
As far above the level of mankind
As here we walk above th'inferior world.

URANIA: So had it need, for dangers are t'ensue,
Enough to shake the constancy of martyrs,
And move the blest inhabitants of heaven.

CARLO: What greater dangers can ensue,
Than what in reaching hither we surmounted?
For, have we not by heaven's supreme decree
Transgressed the bounds established by Alcides?
Have we not insolently dared to plow
The world's uncultivated waste, the ocean,
And dauntlessly explored its dreadful wonders?
And in ascending this ethereal mountain
Stood firm against the fierce assaults of hell,
Repelled more monsters than Alcides vanquished,
And baffled furies, who in horrid shapes
With stormy rage opposed our steep ascent?
And can we now be capable of fear,
In the great cause of heaven? And in a place
Intended for delight, and not for terror?

URANIA: But yet remember, Carlo, that Alcides
Who subdued monsters, triumphed over hell,
Nay, and supponed heaven, became a slave
To pleasure.

UBALDO: Things terrible are enemies to nature, Carlo,
Declared and open enemies,
And all that's great and noble in that nature,
At their approach still rouses to resist them.
But pleasure, though its secret foe,
At least appears its friend.

CARLO: Hark! What enchanting sound salutes my ear?

URANIA: Ay, now the dangerous conflict must begin,
For in this moment hell begins th'attack,
For know thou hear'st no human sounds, the skill
Of all that's exquisite in mortal man,
Could ne'er produce such harmony, the work
Of spirits which usurp th'ethereal air,
Who formerly enjoyed sublimer stations,
And so divinely touched imperial lyres
As pleased, even him who turns th'harmonious spheres,
And sweetly tunes the universe. But see
How yonder fabric like a meteor rises,
The enchanted palace rises to music.
Advancing through the skies its pompous front,
To this enchanting symphony.

CARLO: Hark! Voices in the air.

Musical Entertainment No. 1

Song by one of Armida's spirits, while the enchanted palace is supposed at some little distance to rise.

6
Vn. 1
Vn. 2
Va.
B.c.
12
Vn. 1
Vn. 2
Va.
B.c.
18
Vn. 1
Vn. 2
Va.
B.c.

24
Vn. 1
Vn. 2
Va.
Spirit
B.c.
soft
[soft]
[soft]
[soft]
Ye mighty-y, might-y powers, ye might-y, might-y powers who
28
rule the air, Ye gods, ye gods who in the o- cean dwell, And
31
ye who at the cen- ter gov- ern hell, Hith-er at great Ar- mi- da's call re- pair; And while by your com-

35
Vn. 1
Vn. 2
Va.
Spirit
-mand these towers a- rise, Till with un- e- qualed pomp and state, Their soar-ing heads sa-
[6]
B.c.
39
-lute the skies, Show those a- bove, show those that hell can too cre- ate, Show those a- bove,
44
loud
[loud]
[loud]
show those that hell can too cre- ate.
[loud]
Overture

49
Vn. 1
Vn. 2
Va.
B.c.
55
Vn. 1
Vn. 2
Va.
B.c.
61
1.
2.
Vn. 1
Vn. 2
Va.
B.c.
67
Vn. 1
Vn. 2
Va.
B.c.

72
Vn. 1
Vn. 2
Va.
B.c.
77
82
88

UBALDO: But why, O sacred minister of heaven,
Just at this juncture does this fabric rise?
URANIA: Know to this hour Rinaldo and Armida
Have loosely reveled in enchanted wilds,
And wantoned in the open face of heaven.
But now the enchantress who suspects his constancy,
Has to secure him, by th'advice of hell
Raised this majestic structure.
UBALDO: But can the hero of our age, Rinaldo,
The champion of the Christian cause, Rinaldo,
Descend to love a sorceress?
URANIA: No, not a sorceress, Rinaldo loves
The beauty, not th'enchantress. He loves
The masterpiece of heaven, not that of hell,
The most accomplished work of the Creator;
One who both speaks and looks above a woman,
Whom heaven designed with more peculiar care,
A whole vast species in one single person;
And an idea of sublimer beauty
Than that with which the loveliest of our sex
Ensnare and captivate the souls of men.
CARLO: She is indeed a wonder.
URANIA: A beauty, in the prime of her perfection,
On whom just twenty blooming Eastern springs
Have shed their sweetest influence;
Not an Asiatic monarch but adores her,
But Eastern kings are soft as is their climate.
Have you forgot the time when this Armida,
Leaving her uncle's kingdom of Damascus,
With a dissembled discontent, approached the Christian camp
On the pretence of asking aid
Against the oppression of a tyrant's power?
UBALDO: That curst design we never shall forget,
Which was to weaken and destroy the army,
By drawing all our bravest warriors after her.
URANIA: Tell me, one hero of you all, whose virtue
And whose religion did not melt at sight
Of this triumphant beauty? Nay and melt,
Even as you stood upon the sacred ground.
Where for your lusts a god expired in torments;
Have you so soon forgot this?
UBALDO: Our blushes say we have not.
URANIA: The very rude plebeians of the camp
By habitual hardship mortified to pleasure,
By sanguinary deeds inured to cruelty,
Gazed all the fierceness of their souls away,
And at that sight dissolved in soft desire;
Those brave adventurers whom their fervent zeal,
The flaming love of everlasting glory,
Engaged the noble voluntary champions
Of this renowned crusade, heaven's darling cause,
Disbanded all with shameful stealth by night
And left the field, their glory and their god,
To follow this enchanting fair, of all
Only Rinaldo still remained invincible,
But I want time to say the rest—
Ere yet approaching night usurps the world,
Both thou and Carlo must once more behold her,
And in a cloud with me converse before her,
Unmov'd, unseen, unheard, unthought of by her.
Such is the will of the Most High, but hark!
More harmony, and this way it approaches.
CARLO: And see the happy natives of the place.
URANIA: These are by heaven's permission come to try you,
And with soft sounds seduce your souls to pleasure,
Now stand upon your strongest guards.

Musical Entertainment No. 2

Played and sung by spirits in the shapes of shepherds and shepherdesses [or nymphs], who voluntarily and unknown to Armida attempt to seduce the Christians who came to free Rinaldo from their power.

9
Shep. (B)
bliss- ful swains, The hap- py, hap- py seats, the hap- py, hap- py seats, the hap- py, hap- py seats of
B.c.
13
Ritornello
Vn. 1
Vn. 2
Va.
Shep. (B)
bliss- ful swains.
B.c.
17
Vn. 1
Vn. 2
Va.
Nymph
Wel- come, wel- come, wel- come, wel- come to these bliss-
B.c.
21
Nymph
- ful shades, The soft, soft, soft re- treats of hap- py, hap- py, hap- py, hap- py,
B.c.
25
Nymph
hap- py maids, The soft, soft, soft re- treats of hap- py, hap- py, hap- py, hap- py,
B.c.

Nymph
hap- py maids, The soft, soft, soft re- treats of hap- py, hap- py, hap- py, hap- py,
B.c.
33
Ritornello
Vn. 1
Vn. 2
Va.
Nymph
hap- py maids.
B.c.
[♯3]
37
Vn. 1
soft
Vn. 2
[soft]
Va.
[soft]
SHEPHERDS
S1
Here we feel no want nor care, And no in- clem- en-
S2
Here we feel no want nor care, And no in- clem- en-
B
Here we feel no want nor care, And no in- clem- en-
B.c.
[soft]
[6]

41
Vn. 1
Vn. 2
Va.
SHEPHERDS
S1
-cy of air, And lov- ers nev- er here de- spair. Here we feel no want nor care, And
S2
-cy of air, And lov- ers nev- er here de- spair. Here we feel no want nor care, And
B
-cy of air, And lov- ers nev- er here de- spair. Here we feel no want nor care, And
B.c.
[5]
4 3
6 ♮6
46
Vn. 1
Vn. 2
Va.
SHEPHERDS
S1
no in- clem- en- cy of air, And lov- ers nev- er here de- spair, And lov- ers nev- er
S2
no in- clem- en- cy of air, And lov- ers nev- er here de-spair, And lov- ers nev- er
B
no in-clem- en- cy of air, And lov- ers nev- er here de- spair, And lov- ers nev- er
B.c.
♯4
2
♯3

Ritornello
Vn. 1
Vn. 2
Va.
SHEPHERDS
S1
here de- spair.
S2
here de- spair.
B
here de- spair.
B.c.
Shep. (CT)
Sor- row ev- er from us
flies, Plea- - - sure rev- - els
in our eyes. If we pass an hour in court- ing,
'Tis for more de- li- ci- ous sport- ing, Nev- er cru- el

Shep. (CT)
B.c.
nymph de- nies, No, no, nev- er, no, no, no, no, nev- er cru- el
nymph de- nies, No, no, nev- er, no, no, no, no, nev- er cru- el
Ritornello
Vn. 1
Vn. 2
Va.
nymph de- nies.
Nymph
If an- y- thing like sor- row's seen In our voice, or

104
Nymph
in our mien, 'Tis not grief that gives the anguish, 'Tis with plea- sure,
B.c.
108
Nymph
'tis with plea- sure that we lan- guish; And if ev- er nymph de- nies, 'Tis like
B.c.
112
Nymph
one in love who's wise; 'Tis like one who would in-
B.c.
115
Nymph
-vite To more del- i- cate de- light, 'Tis with wish- ing, dy- ing,
B.c.
119
Nymph
dy- ing, wish- ing, wish- ing, dy- ing eyes, 'Tis with wish- ing, dy- ing,
B.c.
123
Ritornello
Vn. 1
Vn. 2
Va.
Nymph
dy- ing, wish- ing, wish- ing, dy- ing eyes.
B.c.

127
Vn. 1
Vn. 2
Va.
B.c.
132
Vn. 1
Vn. 2
Va.
B.c.
137
Chorus
Vn. 1
Vn. 2
Va.
SHEPHERDS AND NYMPHS
S
All a- bout us and a- bove, Gai- e- ty and love in- spires;
A
All a- bout us and a- bove, Gai- e- ty and love in- spires;
T
All a- bout us and a- bove, Gai- e- ty and love in- spires;
B
All a- bout us and a- bove, Gai- e- ty and love in- spires;
B.c.

142
Vn. 1
Vn. 2
Va.
SHEPHERDS AND NYMPHS
S
All a-bout us and a- bove, All a-bout us and a- bove In- fus- es ten- der-
A
All a-bout us and a- bove, All a-bout us and a- bove In- fus- es ten- der-
T
All a-bout us and a- bove, All a-bout us and a- bove In- fus- es ten- der-
B
All a-bout us and a- bove, All a-bout us and a- bove In- fus- es ten- der-
B.c.
147
-ness and love, And wan- ton fine de- sires. All, all, all, all,
-ness and love, And wan- ton, wan- ton fine de- sires. All, all, all, all,
-ness and love, And wan- ton, wan- ton fine de- sires. All, all, all, all,
-ness and love, And wan- ton, fine de- sires. All, all, all, all,

152
Vn. 1
Vn. 2
Va.
SHEPHERDS AND NYMPHS
S
all a-bout us and a- bove In- fus- es ten- der- ness and love, In- fus- es ten- der-
A
all a-bout us and a- bove In- fus- es ten- der- ness and love, In- fus- es ten- der-
T
all a-bout us and a- bove In- fus- es ten- der- ness and love, In- fus- es ten- der-
B
all a-bout us and a- bove In- fus- es ten- der- ness and love, In- fus- es ten- der-
B.c.
[6]
[7]
[6]
157
Vn. 1
Vn. 2
Va.
SHEPHERDS AND NYMPHS
S
-ness and love, And wan- ton, wan- ton, wan- ton,
A
-ness and love, And wan- ton, wan- ton, wan- ton, wan- ton, wan- ton,
T
-ness and love, And wan- ton, wan- ton, wan- ton, wan- ton,
B
-ness and love, And wan- ton, wan- ton, wan- ton,
B.c.
[7]
[6]

161
Vn. 1
Vn. 2
Va.
SHEPHERDS AND NYMPHS
S
fine de- sires, and wan- ton, wan- ton, wan- ton
A
fine de- sires, and wan- ton, wan- ton, wan- ton, wan- ton, wan- ton
T
fine de- sires, and wan- ton, wan- ton, wan- ton, wan- ton
B
fine de- sires, and wan- ton, wan- ton, wan- ton,
B.c.
5 4 3 [6] [6] [7] [6] [6]
165
Vn. 1
Vn. 2
Va.
SHEPHERDS AND NYMPHS
S
fine de- sires.
A
fine de- sires.
T
fine de- sires.
B
fine de-sires.
B.c.
5 4 3

Shep. (B)
B.c.
170
The jol- ly, jol- ly breeze That comes whist-ling through the trees, From
174
all the bliss-ful re- gion brings Per- fumes up-
177
1.
2.
-on its spic- y wings, The -on its spic- y wings, With its wan-
180
- - ton mo- tion curl- ing curl- ing,
183
curl- ing, curl- ing, curl-ing. The crys-tal rills, Which down, down, down,
186
down, down the hills Run, run, run, run, run

189
Shep. (B)
B.c.
— o'er gold- en — grav- el purl- ing. With its purl- ing.
1.
2.
192
Nymph
All a- round — ve- ne- real
198
tur- tles Coo- ing, bill- ing, on — the — myr- tles; myr- tles;
204
The more they show their am- 'rous trou- ble, More fierce- ly
210
dart their pierc- ing — kiss- es, And more ea- ger- ly re-
216
-dou- ble — The — rap- tures of their murm'r- ing bliss- es. bliss- es.

Urania: Enough, ye ministers of hell be gone,
Behold the waving of this potent wand,
Whose sight can make the fiercest of you tremble,
And whose least touch can with ten thousand plagues
Transfix your howling furies; hence, take hence
Your lying forms, the mimic shapes of men.
Or, by the unutterable name—they vanish.

[Exeunt Spirits.]

Now, heroes, I observed you well, and find,
That you unmoved have passed a dangerous trial,
And gained a glorious conquest o'er yourselves.

Ubaldo: Let us advancing, our success pursue,
They who themselves o'ercome can hell subdue.

Urania: Then as we move towards yonder magic towers,
Protect us in our march ye guardian powers;
Y'immortal ministers to whom by heaven
The care and charge of this great action's given,
Defend us from hell's terrible alarms,
And guard our hearts from pleasure's fatal charms;
Ye angels strike your everlasting lyres,
Sound, sound the lofty trumpet, which inspires
Th'exalted soul with your celestial fires.

[Exeunt all.]

The end of the first act.

The music betwixt the first and second acts begins with a Trumpet Tune, supposed to be played by the same Spirits who played the Overture, but changes with the scene to soft music, and falls gradually to softer, and at last drowsy music, which continues very softly the first ten or twelve lines of the second act.

Act 2

Scene: The inside of the enchanted palace.

Enter Phenissa [and] Nisroe; Rinaldo [is] sleeping on a couch.

Phenissa: Sleeps he secure? And is the Queen obeyed?
Though here's a magic symphony might lull
The raving furies into soft repose.

Nisroe: There he lies buried in eternal sleep,
Unless myself or some more powerful spirit
Unbind and rouse him from his iron slumber.
Thrice while I muttered mystic sounds I sprinkled
His temples with the drowsy deadly dew,
Brushed by th'infernal raven's baleful wing
From the black poppies which on Lethe grow.
How fares Armida?

Phenissa: She dotes, alas, she dotes on this Rinaldo,
Her love, and fear of losing what she loves
Disquiet her sometimes almost to madness,
Thou know'st the greatness of her soul;
from whence
Conclude how this tempestuous flame must shake her;
Alas, I pity her.

Nisroe: I cannot blame thee.
Even I, who for these long six thousand years
Have never felt one motion like remorse,
I, were I not a devil, I should pity her;
The fairest creature which on this side heaven
My eyes have e'er beheld.

Phenissa: Say, what success attends this desperate love?

Nisroe: Alas, I dare not; for remember Ramiel,
Who but for barely hinting at her fate,
Lies howling at the bottom of th'abyss,
Under the vengeance of that dreadful god,
Who makes even furies tremble;
Scourged till at each resounding stroke
He bellows to the blow:
While all around, the poor tormented ghosts,
Gastfully staring with their baleful eyes,
Cease their shrill cries, and their lamenting wails;
All with amazement hushed, and as they listen,
Shuddering with horror at his hideous roar,
Yet what I dare, I'll tell thee.
Fame, that with indefatigable wings
Borne through the boundless regions of the air,
Incessantly surveys this globe of earth,
Once in the course of the revolving year,
Stoops at these Isles of Fortune, the abodes
Of happy heroes, separated souls,
To visit her adopted sons, all demigods,
Who, undisturbed in these Elysian shades,
Pursue immortal pleasure. If he shrinks not
When next the goddess comes, he's ours forever.

Phenissa: When arrives she?

Nisroe: I dare no more, but 'tis thy part to try
To cure Armida of this raging passion.

Phenissa: Nay, then thou sayest enough; alas, I have,
Thou know'st it is my interest more than hers;
Rinaldo is a Christian,
And wins each moment on Armida's soul,
Who knows how far at last he may prevail?
If he should once seduce her from her faith,
What could be so abandoned as Phenissa?
It is my daily study to reclaim her,
A thousand times in vain I have attempted it.

Nisroe: Once more attempt it, then if thou succeed'st not,
Lull her with hope, true woes are to succeed,
Let her enjoy false pleasures while she may.
But she appears, I vanish.

[Nisroe] sinks.

Enter Armida.

Armida: Phenissa, sleeps Rinaldo?

Phenissa: He does.
Why were you absent at the magic rites?

Armida: I hate this cursed art since first it showed me
That, that to which the hardest things are possible,
Yet wants the power to calm my raging grief;
All nature lies subjected to my charms,
I give her rest, and rouse her with alarms,
My arbitrary voice she hears with awe,
And standing fixed suspends th'eternal law.
I to the tempest make the poles resound,
And the conflicting elements confound;
At my command
The thunder rushes out on flaming wings,
And all the hollow deep of hell

With hideous uproar rings;
Fierce spirits who great heaven's command disdained,
Submit themselves and are by mine restrained.
The wildest things are by my power confined:
All but my wild ungovernable mind.
But I have homebred furies which rebel,
While I subdue the fiercest powers of hell.
Oh, my foreboding soul!
PHENISSA: Compose yourself, consider you're a queen.
ARMIDA: Consider I'm a slave, consider I'm a lover.
PHENISSA: No common queen, they rule but common slaves;
You govern with a nod all Asia's monarchs.
ARMIDA: Effeminate, slothful, lukewarm creatures all,
Whose souls were but half-kindled by their maker.
PHENISSA: Then what they want from heaven they have from you;
Your eyes have blown those souls into a flame.
ARMIDA: Those kings I scorned before I knew my hero;
What are those royal pageants? Thou hast seen them,
And what is my Rinaldo? Thou hast gazed on him.
PHENISSA: The greatest of mankind, since to this height
The great Armida by her favors raised him;
Before, the last of the Italian princes.
ARMIDA: But the first of conquerors.
PHENISSA: A private man, without comannd in th'army.
ARMIDA: Fortune, and Fame, and Victory obeyed him,
Him, the sole power of that victorious army.
Who was the terror of the East, but he?
This private man made all your monarchs tremble,
Even in the midst of their own shivering slaves,
To whom they owed their power and their security.
His power was in himself, his dauntless soul,
And his unconquered own right hand his safety.
What? Though he rules no empire, he deserves one,
And has both conquered and rejected crowns:
He in his inborn worth is more exalted.
No drowsy monarch by a dull descent,
But for his high desert preferred by heaven,
And singled from the rest of humankind,
To execute the vast designs of fate.
PHENISSA: The theme transports you.
ARMIDA: 'Tis my love transports me.
PHENISSA: 'Tis frankly owned,
For such a proud, severe, disdainful beauty.
ARMIDA: Yes, I am proud that I myself have excellence,
To know and love such merit; surely love
In this excess has something that's divine;
Women who dote on monsters even to madness,
Are proud of their own fury. What must I be,
When the consenting world admires my choice?
Thou, whose cold mass runs curdling through thy veins,
Thou gazest on Rinaldo with desire;
Yet thou hast only seen the god of love,
In the fresh beauties of my blooming hero:
Oh, even in thee, what raptures had he raised!
Hadst thou once seen him like the god of war,
While grizzly terror perched upon his plume;
Severely shining in his dreadful helmet,
And thundering through the tempest of the field.
PHENISSA: Well! Though you love with fury, you possess;
Since then the god of love has made you blest,
Why should you toil to make yourself unhappy?
ARMIDA: Once more, I tell thee, love has taught me fear.
PHENISSA: Fear! Fear of what?
ARMIDA: The torments which the souls in hell endure;
Nay worse, those souls have only missed of heaven,
But to have lost it, that's the plague of devils.
PHENISSA: You seek those groundless fears.
ARMIDA: Ah no!
Hell threatened me with fate by Ramiel's voice,
And heaven by these foreboding thoughts foretells it;
And, what is more than heaven or hell to me,
Rinaldo has confirmed it.
PHENISSA: 'Tis but an hour since he declared he loved you.
ARMIDA: But with such accents and such eyes declared it,
His very anger had been less provoking;
Can one who loves with such a soul as mine,
Be tortured worse than with endearing words,
Spoke with the coldness of that cruel air?
PHENISSA: But how should nature bear perpetual rapture,
When the quire sinks in momentary transports?
Sometimes he meets your love with equal fury.
ARMIDA: If he did not, he would be less than man,
This desert isle divides us from the world,
Where he, and I, and thou, are humankind:
He loved me not in Palestine, where I
Seduced the very flower of Godfrey's army,
Subdued their inmost souls by my soft arts;
And led them from the army through the East
In amorous pomp, the common foes of Asia,
And victims to my uncle's great revenge,
Only Rinaldo's soul remained impregnable;
A fiercer flame than that of love had seized it,
And his eyes sparkled with severer fires;
The love of glory reigned sole tyrant there,
Which in great souls still rages to a fault,
The crime of angels, and of men like angels;
Who conscious to their own surpassing excellence,
Would by great actions force the envious world
T'acknowledge their transcendency of nature.
PHENISSA: But still the ambitious love, as well as others;
Nature makes use of love in mighty minds,
Who else would be aspiring to be gods,
To show them they are men.
ARMIDA: Yes, they can love, but think that love their frailty,
And not their virtue;
And when that love comes once t'obstruct ambition,

With all their might they make a vast effort,
And tear it from their souls.
PHENISSA: The knowing this,
One would have thought, might have secured your heart.
ARMIDA: This made me dote on him, and as he slept
Transport him on a storm's sonorous wings,
Far from the war, and the shrill trumpet's sound,
To this sweet place designed for love and joy.
Yet even here, where earth and heaven, nay hell
Conspires t'indulge the sweetest of all passions;
Where even I, for whom a thousand lovers
Have sighed, and sighed in vain, with all that's soft
And delicate in love descend t'incite him,
Even here he has but intervals of passion;
'Tis true those intervals are furious all,
For he in everything is more than mortal:
But then anon, even in my very arms,
My eager arms, he languishes for glory:
He meditates profound, and fetches sighs,
Which, while he vainly struggles to repress,
With terrible revulsions shake his soul:
With eyes upon me fixed he sees me not,
And gazing upon his, I find him absent.
Oft in his sleep he takes convulsive starts,
And cries, "To arms, hark, hark, the trumpet sounds,
And Glory calls to arms; I come, I fly,
Thou darling of my soul, thou mistress even of gods!"
Then with the fury of the transport waking,
He fetches sighs that shake his inmost soul.
PHENISSA: Well, since ambition rules in all great souls,
Shake off this softer rage.
ARMIDA: I want the very will to shake it off,
Ambition rules in men, but love prevails in women;
Had heaven, that gave us such attractive grace,
Not tempered our unruly souls with love,
We had been more dangerous to men than devils:
Phenissa, I am a woman.
PHENISSA: But no vulgar woman.
ARMIDA: No, nor is mine a vulgar passion,
I bear a mind no stranger to ambition,
But still my love prevails above my pride.
Oh, let me never know indifference more;
I never can, nor will be calm again;
For who could live indifferent as to heaven,
That had but known the vast delight of gods,
And had a taste of immortality?
PHENISSA: 'Tis the mere fever of your mind that talks thus,
For love is nothing else.
ARMIDA: Thou rail'st at love as fiends blaspheme their god,
Because he has abandoned thee forever.
PHENISSA: My years will bring my sentiments to you.
ARMIDA: Oh never, never let me see those years,
The soul, that sparkle of celestial fire,
The longer it has lain immersed in matter,
The colder feels its sense of heaven and love,
The great originals from which it sprung.
PHENISSA: Reason requires that you should rule this passion.
ARMIDA: Talk not of reason; what, but love, is reason?
For what, but love, is happiness?
Love first appears with reason in the soul,
And by degrees with reason it decays.
But cease, forbear thy foolish, ill-timed counsel,
With silent awe attend my potent charm.
And thou, O air, that murmurest on the mountain,
Be hushed at my command, silence ye winds,
That make outrageous war upon the ocean;
And thou, old Ocean, lull thy wondering waves;
Ye warring elements be hushed as death,
While I impose my dread commands on hell;
And thou profoundest hell, whose dreadful sway
Is given to me, by fate and Demogorgon,
Hear, hear, my powerful voice through all thy regions!
By Demogorgon, I command thee, hear!
And from thy gloomy caverns thunder thy reply.
Subterranean thunder [sounds from beneath the stage].
I am obeyed—
Now send up dreams that may be fittest found
T'impose upon Rinaldo's slumbering thoughts,
And to enslave his soul.

Musical Entertainment No. 3

Made by dreams that at Armida's command appear in order to the terrifying [of] Rinaldo, in the shapes of Bertoldo and Sophia, parents to the hero; and in the likeness of several whom Rinaldo had slain in battle.

12
Vn. 1
Vn. 2
Va.
B.c.
18
Soph.
Bert.
Ri- nal- do!
Ri- nal- do! Look up, look up, look up, be-
23
-hold the mourn- ful shade Of him who gave thee breath, Who steps to see thee, while thou'r-
27
laid Up- on the con- fines here of death; T'in- form thee of thy fu- ture state, And ere

32
Soph.
Look up, look up my son, look up- on
Bert.
yet it be too late, To pre- vent thy wretch-ed fate.
B.c.
38
me, In me th'af-flict- ed Soph- ia see. Ah, son! Not all the grind- ing
♮6 ♮3 ♮3 [♮3]
44
throes, With which, when thou wert born, My tor- tured nerves were torn, E-qualed half the wrack-ing
[6]
50
woes, Which now thy moth- er un- der- goes, Thou dar- ling of my soul, thou dar- ling of my
♮3 ♮3
56
soul, for thee, Thou dar- ling of my soul, thou dar- ling of my soul, for thee.
♮3 ♮3
63
Last night, last night I cast a look Up- on fate's dread- ful book, And read a
6 6 5 [♮6]

69
Bert.
les- son which no brain That is mor- tal can sus- tain, While all my soul, while all my soul with hor- ror
B.c.
75
Soph.
Oh, oh, the dis- trac- tion, oh, oh, oh, oh, the dis- trac- tion of the
Bert.
shook.
B.c.
83
Soph.
sight! And oh, oh, oh, the tor- ments, the tor-
B.c.
89
Soph.
- ments of the fright! I nev- er shall for- get, no, no, no, no, nev- er, no, no, no, no,
B.c.
96
Soph.
nev- er, nev- er shall for- get that night, no, no, no, nev- er, no, no, nev- er, no, no,
B.c.
102
Soph.
nev- er, nev- er shall for- get that night.
3
Bert.
Rouse all thy fac- ul- ties, my son, And to my
B.c.

Bert.
B.c.
fa- tal words give ear, For know that they con- cern thee near; No lon- ger let thy
fan- cy run Af- ter that air- y phan- tom Fame; But love Ar- mi- da, love Ar- mi- da
with a con- stant, con- stant flame: Or des- ti- ny de- crees, Thou shalt feel
woes, which but to hear Would dis- tract thy soul with fear, And all, all, all thy
blood, all thy blood with hor- ror freeze, And all, all, all thy
Soph.
Ah! See, see a- round the rav- ing
blood, all thy blood with hor- ror freeze.

140
Soph.
hosts Of pur- ple ghosts Whose blood thou hast in bat- tle spilt With fear- ful guilt, Who, un- less
B.c.
145
Soph.
awed by her com- mand- ing power, Would, ah, this mo- ment tear thee and de- vour!
Bert.
How they ad-
B.c.
4 3
151 (Dance begins.)
Bert.
-vance with whirl- ing brands, All flam- ing in their threat'n- ing hands! And as they go their dread- ful
B.c.
♯3
[♯3]
155
Chorus
(During the chorus a dance of spirits.)
Vn. 1
Vn. 2
Va.
Bert.
round, Re- venge, re- venge re- sound!
SPIRITS
S
For re- venge, re-
A
For re- venge, re-
T
For re- venge, re-
B
For re- venge, re-
B.c.
♯3
♯3
♯3
[♯3]

160
Vn. 1
Vn. 2
Va.
S
-venge, re- venge, re- venge to Ar- mi- da we call, That we ter- ri- bly may on our
A
-venge, re- venge, re- venge to Ar- mi- da we call, That we ter- ri- bly may on our
T
-venge, re- venge, re- venge to Ar- mi- da we call, That we ter- ri- bly may on our
B
-venge, re- venge, re- venge to Ar- mi- da we call, That we ter- ri- bly may on our
SPIRITS
B.c.
[6]
[7]
168
Vn. 1
Vn. 2
Va.
S
mur- der- er fall; That as now we with sul- phu- rous torch- es sur- round him, We with our
A
mur- der- er fall; That as now we with sul- phu- rous torch- es sur- round him, We with our
T
mur- der- er fall; That as now we with sul- phu- rous torch- es sur- round him, We with our
B
mur- der- er fall; That as now we with sul- phu- rous torch- es sur- round him, We with our
SPIRITS
B.c.
♯3
[6]
♯6
♯3
♯6

ARMIDA: By heaven Rinaldo smiles at all their threats,
And slumbering scorns this terrible appearance.
Confusion and amazement! What do I hear?
Fame's trumpet [sounds].
What trumpets, this whose great and martial sound
Makes the world echo to its music?
Ha! Disappeared! All vanished on the sudden!
Spirits vanish.
Gone undismissed! The charm not yet unbound!
Ho! Arioc! Hear, and know my awful voice,
At my command appear again I charge thee,
Or else be banished from my sight forever.
[Arioc becomes visible.]
ARIOC: *(half rising)* O Queen, to whom thy excellence of nature,
And thy transcendent beauty gives command
O'er all th'infernal powers, for in thy brightness
We see what once we were in our high stations,
And some reflected beams enjoy
Of that supremely blissful vision,
From whose enjoyment our aspiring minds
Have banished us forever.
Excuse thy slaves unable to obey thee,
For know a greater power now drives us hence.
One of the brightest of th'imperial mansions
Expels us with a stream of light
That sets this atmosphere on fire,
And with its blaze insufferably bright
Confounds hell's gloomy powers;
Summon th'aerial spirits to thy aid,
For they who poised upon expanded wings,
Like basking in the sun's meridian glory,
Are fitter to sustain heavens flaming ministers
Than we who sojourn the dusky deep;
And they, perhaps too, with enchanting voices,
To pleasure may seduce Rinaldo's soul.
Pleasure thou know'st can tame that dauntless soul,
Which thou no more by terrors canst subdue,
Than fright the dreadful god who darts the thunder.
But oh, dismiss me, for I can no more,
A deluge of imperial light o'erwhelms me.
ARMIDA: Begone then, and for ease to hell repair.
[Arioc] vanishes.
But see Rinaldo wakens. Oh, astonishment!
How everything I see and hear confounds me,
And shows a power above my own controls me.
Let us retire, and then unseen observe him,
I from himself my destiny would learn.
Rinaldo rises from the couch; Armida and Phenissa retire to the side of the stage.
RINALDO: Methought the trumpet's noble sound

Alarmed me to the combat.
Was it illusion that, or was it real?
Let it be what it will, it gives thee cause
To ask thyself this question, what thou wert,
And what thou art at present? O Rinaldo,
Heaven gave thee reason for thy guide of action,
But that's a lamp set up in every breast.
Heaven gave thee yet a more exalted spirit
Which reached above the frail efforts of reason;
For reason only teaches man his duty:
That raised thy freeborn soul to nobler heights,
To things superlatively great and good,
Beyond what reason or what heaven required.
But where's that spirit now? That towering faculty,
Which mounting soared above humanity?
'Tis now half quenched by an ignobler fire.
Oh, base desertion from myself and glory.

ARMIDA: Hear this, Phenissa, now are my fears groundless?

RINALDO: Nay, thou hast stifled too the very dictates
Of common reason which mankind obeys,
And while ten thousand slaves before Jerusalem,
Urged by their duty in this very moment,
To danger and to death bid loud defiance,
Thou loiter'st here in soft inglorious ease.
Perhaps the fable of the army, ha!
Canst thou bear that? Canst thou so much as think
That thou deserv'st to be condemned and live?

ARMIDA: Oh, I am lost, beyond all hope, undone?

RINALDO: Nay, canst thou bear even this? That thou no more
Deserv'st to be preferred above the rest,
Above the rest, admired? That in this moment
The brave Tancredi like celestial Jove
With thunder in his hand distributes fate,
While thou—by heaven, I'd rather be a dog,
And lead a brutal life, without reflection
Than to be stung with the tormenting thought
That one who is my fellow creature
Merits to command me.
Oh, what's become of that aspiring greatness
That once disdained to yield to less than infinite?
'Tis lost, 'tis to a woman's will abandoned.

PHENISSA: Madam, contain yourself.

RINALDO: 'Tis true, thou lov'st her with that height of fury,
Which none but her inimitable beauties
Could ever have inspired.

PHENISSA: Observe him now.

RINALDO: But what? The vulgar can command small passions;
'Tis for Rinaldo to control the fiercest.
Why art thou by Fame's hundred tongues extolled?
Why by her golden trump proclaimed a hero,
If thou hast only brutal force to boast of?
'Tis chiefly force of mind that makes a hero.
Then, O thou loveliest of thy sex, Armida,
Thou only one of all created beings,
That e'er had power to fire Rinaldo's heart,
Be satisfied with this, that only thou
Hadst power to move his soul, which for a time
Admired thee equal to eternal glory.

Fame's trumpet [sounds,] and voices [sing].

Rinaldo, in the enchanted grove
Prepare to meet immortal Love;
Straight to the bower of bliss repair,
Fortune and Fame attend thee there.

RINALDO: Again that noble clangor, and with voices!
Nay, then 'tis evident, 'tis no illusion.
Who e'er thou art that with those godlike sounds
Thus raisest all that's powerful in my nature,
This moment in th'enchanted grove I'll meet thee.
But, O Rinaldo, whither wert thou fallen?
Who want'st a call to rouse thee from thy lethargy,
That might awake the dead and make them start
From their eternal slumbers.

Exit [Rinaldo].

ARMIDA: Patience, ye heavens, or thou hell, revenge!
But let us to th'enchanted grove repair,
And thither call the powers that rule the air;
Yet lest the charms of pleasure too should fail,
Hell, let thy gloomy gods their last efforts prepare,
If destiny decrees that after all,
I needs must perish, like myself I'll fall;
I'll fall like one whose arbitrary sway,
Th'aerial and th'infernal gods obey;
With me the traitor shall not only die,
But groaning nature in convulsions lie.

[Voices sing.]

Now to the bower of bliss let's fly
And all the way we go,
Hell, by thy music show
Thou art enraged as well as I.

[Exeunt all.]

The end of the second act.

The Act Tune . . . begins with terrible music, supposed to be played by the Infernal Spirits, partly at Armida's command, and partly to express their resentment for Rinaldo's behavior. With the scene the music changes to soft and gay.

Act 3

Scene: The enchanted wilderness.
Soft music, Rinaldo solu[s].

RINALDO: Were then those glorious voices but delusions,
That called me with that pomp of noble harmony?
Fortune they cried, and Fame attended here,
But all things here as soft as lovers' wishes,
This magic symphony with sweetness soothes me,
And everything around me breathes desire,
Which passes through my senses to my soul,
And to Armida's beauteous image there
Imparts fresh force and new divinity.
That image too perpetually torments me,

Reflecting on th'ecstatic joys,
Which I must lose forever.
Enter Armida and Phenissa.
ARMIDA: See where he walks in gloomy contemplation?
Summon th'aerial spirits to their duty,
While I unseen observe him.
RINALDO: Couldst thou resolve, then should heaven send the occasion
To leave this lovely masterpiece of nature;
To leave her in this fullness of desire,
This height of all thy furious wishes;
When each succeeding hour
Adds to her graces, and sublimes thy pleasure.
Canst thou resolve to see that face no more;
And nevermore to hear that voice,
Whose music charms above the magic songs
Even of th'immortal ministers who serve her?
Canst thou resolve? Ay, there's the dreadful question!
For what can be so terrible to nature
As to fall all at once from blissful rapture
To the curst state of wishing without hope?
Canst thou make this effort and live? No matter,
Life's not the thing in question now, 'tis glory.
ARMIDA: See how the tempest of his passion tears him!
But canst thou hear him thus contrive thy ruin,
And yet stand tamely by?
Thou who canst crush him in a moment!
Since thou hast cloyed him with thy softness,
What if he heard thee thunder in his ears,
With that terrible voice that untunes nature,
And makes th'inverted spheres fall into discord?
But something tender in my soul restrains me,
Is it compassion? No, 'tis something softer,
Thou lov'st the traitor still; lov'st him to madness.
I do, I will, I must. Can ever woman
Behold that form without a bleeding heart?
That mien that claims the empire of the universe?
With which he may give laws to humankind.
May the high place with dignity maintain
Of heaven's great viceroy for this underworld,
And represent immortal majesty.
Once more I'll try endearments. *(She comes forward.)*
RINALDO: *(perceiving her)* Ha! The Queen!
Now, where are all thy feeble resolutions?
One glance has humbled thy aspiring thoughts,
Pleasure flows streaming from those lovely eyes,
And with its sweetness overcomes my soul.
If 'tis a crime to look and be transported,
Why was I made thus sensible to pleasure?
Why was she formed with that surpassing beauty,
That might transport an angel from his sphere,
And fix him by divine resemblance here?
Armida! My Queen! My mistress!
ARMIDA: Yes, she is here, and still the same she has been,
Unless that to herself she's altered;
That I must see, *(pulls out a glass and looks in it)*
At least I'm sure she is the same to thee;
But thou art altered to thyself and me,
And thou art lost to both.
RINALDO: So lost indeed I was, while I
From thee, the dearer part of me, was absent;
But I shall find myself again in thee.
(to her looking in the glass) Why dost thou vainly seek thy likeness there?
Can the frail crystal represent divinity?
Wouldst thou behold these eyes in all their glories?
To see the force of their celestial fire,
Turn them on mine all flaming with desire;
Or look upon the crystal of the skies,
And view thy own in the world's flaming eyes;
Those eyes which vast intelligences move
Minds made like thine, all knowledge and all love.
ARMIDA: By all my hopes of happiness and him,
His heart's once more my own. Rinaldo sit,
To drive away all sorrow from thy soul
I'll give thee music that may lull despair,
And tempt the dire tormentors of the damned,
With lifted brands to listen to its air.
Aerial spirits who attend me, hear,
And shaped like gods whom Greece adored, appear.

Musical Entertainment No. 4

Made by spirits, who at Armida's command appear to entertain Rinaldo in the shapes of Venus, Cupid, and a chorus of loves [and graces]. Venus is discovered reclined on a couch, with her attendants of loves about her, and singing in soft complaining notes.

Fl. 1
Fl. 2
Venus
B.c.
Cu- pid, Cu- pid, come to the re- lief Of thy moth- er's pierc- ing
grief; Cu- pid, Cu- pid, come to the re-

Fl. 1
Fl. 2
Venus
B.c.
-lief Of thy moth- er's pierc- ing_ grief; Hith- er,_ Cu- pid,
quick- ly_ fly; With thee bring thy keen- est_ dart, To sub- due a reb- el heart,
Thou art_ scorned, thou art scorned, thou art scorned as well as_ I, Thou_ art scorned,
thou_ art scorned as well_ as_ I.

51
[Chorus]
Fl. 1
Fl. 2
Vn. 2
Va.
S
A
T
B
LOVES AND GRACES
Come, come, come, come, come, come, come, come,
Come, come, come, come, come,
Come,
B.c.
[4] [♯3] ♯3
56
Vn. 1
Vn. 2
Va.
S
A
T
B
LOVES AND GRACES
Come, come, come, come, come, come, come, come Cu- pid, come, come, come, come, come
come, come, come, come, come Cu- pid, come, come, come, come,
come, come, come, come, come, come Cu- pid, come, come, come, come,
come, come, come, come, come, come, come, come, come, come, come Cu- pid, come, come, come, come, come
B.c.
6 6 ♯3 6 6 ♮3 4 2

61
Vn. 1
Vn. 2
Va.
S
Cu- pid, on thy gold- en wing, And in thy sound- ing quiv- er, and
A
come Cu- pid, on thy gold- en wing, And in thy sound- ing
T
come Cu- pid, on thy gold- en wing, And in thy sound- ing
B
Cu- pid, on thy gold- en wing, And in thy sound- ing
LOVES AND GRACES
B.c.
[6]
5 3 4 2 4 2 3 6
66
Vn. 1
Vn. 2
Va.
S
in thy sound- ing quiv- er, and in thy sound- ing quiv- er bring Per- ni- cious
A
quiv- er, and in thy sound- ing quiv- er, and in thy quiv- er bring Per- ni- cious
T
quiv- er, and in thy sound- ing quiv- er, and in thy quiv- er bring Per- ni- cious
B
quiv- er, and in thy sound- ing quiv- er, and in thy quiv- er bring Per- ni- cious
LOVES AND GRACES
B.c.
[6] 6 6 6 6 [6]

71
Vn. 1
Vn. 2
Va.
S
ar- rows winged with fire, And in thy sound- ing quiv- er, and in thy sound- ing
A
ar- rows winged with fire, And in thy sound- ing quiv- er, and
T
ar- rows winged with fire, And in thy sound- ing quiv- er, and
B
ar- rows winged with fire, And in thy sound- ing quiv- er, and
LOVES AND GRACES
B.c.
♮3 [6] ♮3 5 3 4 2 4 2 3 6 6
76
Vn. 1
Vn. 2
Va.
S
quiv- er, and in thy sound- ing, sound- ing quiv- er bring Per- ni- cious ar- rows winged with
A
in thy sound- ing quiv- er, and in thy quiv- er bring Per- ni- cious ar- rows winged with
T
in thy sound- ing quiv- er, and in thy quiv- er bring Per- ni- cious ar- rows winged with
B
in thy sound- ing quiv- er, and in thy quiv- er bring Per- ni- cious ar- rows winged with
LOVES AND GRACES
B.c.
6 6 [4 3] [6] ♮3

81
Vn. 1
Vn. 2
Va.
S
A
T
B
LOVES AND GRACES
fire, T'in- flict in- cur- - a- ble de- sire, T'in- flict in- cur-
fire, T'in- flict, in- flict in- cur- a- ble de- sire, T'in- flict in-
fire, T'in- flict, in- flict in- cur- a- ble de- sire, T'in- flict in-
fire, T'in- flict, in- cur- - a- ble de- sire, T'in- flict in- cur-
B.c.
86
Symphony
- a- ble de- sire.
-cur- a- ble de- sire.
-cur- a- ble de- sire.
- a- ble de- sire.

91
Vn. 1
Vn. 2
Va.
B.c.
97
Cupid
1.
2.
Thus fly- ing through the balm- y
102
air, To my great par- ent I re- pair; And though the world's main-tained by
106
me, Yet, Moth- er, to at- tend on thee, I leave the might- y care.
Venus
A

111
Cupid
Venus
B.c.
I'll
mor- tal in this fra- grant bower, Pre- sumes that he's a- bove our__ power.
[6]
[6 4 5] 3
115
make that mor- tal know, I'll make that mor- tal know, That none, none, no none, none too
♯3
[♮]6
121
great for Love__ can__ grow; I tame the might- y, might- y powers a-
♯3
[♯3]
[♯3]
♯3
♯4 2
[6]
[7]
[♯3]
126
-bove, And cru- el, cru- el,__ cru- el gods be- low,
♯3
[♯3]
6 4
[5] ♯3
131
I tame the might- y, might- y powers a- bove, And cru- el,
♯3
[♯3]
♯3
[♯4 2]
7
♯3
[♯3]
136
Ritornello
Vn. 1
Vn. 2
Va.
cru- el,__ cru- el gods be- low.
[♯3]
6 4
[5] ♯3
♯3

141
Vn. 1
Vn. 2
Va.
Cupid
Great Jove, whose arms the light- ning fling, Has felt my fierc- er fire, And
B.c.
146
[Chorus]
Vn. 1
Vn. 2
Va.
Cupid
hell's in- ex- o- ra- ble king Has yield- ed to de- sire.
LOVES AND GRACES
S
Great Jove, great
A
Great Jove, great
T
Great Jove, great
B
Great Jove, great
B.c.

151
Vn. 1
Vn. 2
Va.
S
Jove, whose arms the light- ning fling, Has felt thy fierc- - er
A
Jove, whose arms the light- ning fling, Has felt, has felt thy fierc- er, fierc- er
T
Jove, whose arms the light- ning fling, Has felt, has felt thy fierc- er, fierc- er
B
Jove, whose arms the light- ning fling, Has felt thy fierc- - er
LOVES AND GRACES
B.c.

156
Vn. 1
Vn. 2
Va.
S
fire, And hell, hell's in- ex- o- ra- ble king Has yield- ed to de-
A
fire, And hell, hell's in- ex- o- ra- ble king Has yield- ed to de-
T
fire, And hell, hell's in- ex- o- ra- ble king Has yield- ed to de-
B
fire, And hell, hell's in- ex- o- ra- ble king Has yield- ed to de-
LOVES AND GRACES
B.c.

161
Vn. 1
Vn. 2
Va.
S
-sire, Has yield- ed to de- sire, And hell, hell's in- ex- o- ra- ble
A
-sire, Has yield- ed to de- sire, And hell, hell's in- ex- o- ra- ble
T
-sire, Has yield- ed to de- sire, And hell, hell's in- ex- o- ra- ble
B
-sire, Has yield- ed to de- sire, And hell, hell's in- ex- o- ra- ble
LOVES AND GRACES
B.c.

166
Vn. 1
Vn. 2
Va.
S
king Has yield- ed to de- sire, Has yield- ed to de- sire.
A
king Has yield- ed to de- sire, Has yield- ed to de- sire.
T
king Has yield- ed to de- sire, Has yield- ed to de- sire.
B
king Has yield- ed to de- sire, Has yield- ed to de- sire.
LOVES AND GRACES
B.c.

171
Cupid
But let us cease our soar- ing strains, Love con- quers most when he com- plains. Now
B.c.
176
Cupid
quick- ly, quick- ly, quick- ly through th'en- chant- ed grove, Let all
B.c.
181
Cupid
my nim- ble breth- ren rove, Now quick- ly, quick- ly, quick- ly through th'en-
B.c.
186
Cupid
-chant- ed grove, Let all my nim- ble breth- ren
B.c.
191
Cupid
rove, Let all my nim- ble breth- ren rove.
B.c.
196
Chaconne
Vn. 1
Vn. 2
Va.
B.c.

202
Fl. 1
Fl. 2
Vn. 1
Vn. 2
Va.
B.c.
[7] 4 ♯3
209
Fl. 1
Fl. 2
Vn. 1
Vn. 2
Va.
B.c.
[5]
[6]
214
Vn. 1
Vn. 2
Va.
B.c.
♯3
[6]

218
Fl. 1
Fl. 2
Vn. 1
Vn. 2
Va.
B.c.
♯3
224
Fl. 1
Fl. 2
Vn. 1
Vn. 2
Va.
B.c.
[5 6]
229
Vn. 1
Vn. 2
Va.
B.c.
[5 6]
♯3
[5 6]

233
Fl. 1
Fl. 2
Vn. 1
Vn. 2
Va.
B.c.
[5 6]
♯3
239
Fl. 1
Fl. 2
Vn. 1
Vn. 2
Va.
B.c.
245
Vn. 1
Vn. 2
Va.
B.c.
[6]
♯3

249
Fl. 1
Fl. 2
Vn. 1
Vn. 2
Va.
B.c.
[6]
♯3
253
Fl. 1
Fl. 2
Va.
B.c.
257
Fl. 1
Fl. 2
Vn. 1
Vn. 2
Va.
B.c.
5 6
7 6
7 6

262
Vn. 1
Vn. 2
Va.
B.c.
267
Fl. 1
Fl. 2
Vn. 1
Vn. 2
Va.
B.c.
273
Fl. 1
Fl. 2
Vn. 1
Vn. 2
Va.
B.c.

278
Venus
Let earth, and air, and flood, and fire, And ev- 'ry thing a-
B.c.
4 ♯3 [♯3] [♯3] ♮3 6
282
Venus
-round con- spire To breathe forth soft and sweet de- sire, Let earth, and air, and
B.c.
♯3 ♯3 [♯3] 6 4 ♯3 3 ♮3 ♮4 2 [♮6]
286
Venus
flood, and fire, And ev- 'ry thing a- round con- spire To breathe forth soft and
B.c.
6 6 [♮6] ♯3
[Chorus]
290
Vn. 1
Vn. 2
Va.
Venus
sweet de- sire. Let sweet de- sire.
LOVES AND GRACES
S
Let earth, and air, and flood, and fire, And
A
Let earth, and air, and flood, and fire, And
T
Let earth, and air, and flood, and fire, And
B
Let earth, and air, and flood, and fire, And
B.c.
1. 2.
5 ♯3 5 ♯3 ♯3 [6] ♯3 [♮3]

294
Vn. 1
Vn. 2
Va.
S
ev- 'ry thing a- round con- spire To breathe forth soft_ and_ sweet de- sire, Let
A
ev- 'ry thing a- round con- spire To breathe forth soft and sweet de- sire. Let
T
ev- 'ry thing a- round con- spire To breathe forth soft and sweet de- sire. Let
B
ev- 'ry thing a- round con- spire To breathe forth soft_ and_ sweet de- sire. Let
LOVES AND GRACES
B.c.
[6] ♯3 ♯3 6 4 ♯3 ♯3
298
Vn. 1
Vn. 2
Va.
S
earth, and air, and flood, and fire, And ev- 'ry_ thing a- round con- spire To
A
earth, and air, and flood, and fire, And ev- 'ry thing a- round con- spire To
T
earth, and air, and flood, and fire, And ev- 'ry thing a- round con- spire To
B
earth, and air, and flood, and fire, And ev- 'ry thing a- round con- spire To
LOVES AND GRACES
B.c.
♮3 ♮4 2 [♮6] [6] [2] [♮6]

Enter Urania, Ubaldo, and Carlo.

URANIA: Thus we unseen have passed the winding mazes
Of this enchanted labyrinth, and now
Stand here invisible to mortal sight,
To all unless Rinaldo's.
See where the wanton lovers lie reclined
In all the soft and pleasing pomp of luxury.
But now 'tis heaven's high will that I retire,
And the remaining task consign to you:
(to Carlo) To you, I delegate this sacred wand,
This wand whose powerful touch no impious spirit,
Whether of earth, or air, or fire can bear,
With which thou shalt expel these shining phantoms.
Then, waiting the departure of the enchantress,
Ubaldo, thou shalt first approach Rinaldo,
And to his eyes presenting that bright orb,
Show him himself, the only form can shake him.
Exit [Urania].

Carlo goes round waving his wand, and the spirits vanish.

ARMIDA: What? All upon the wing? And undismissed too!
All starting with amazement from their stations,
Like watchful fowl, that spring upon descrying
The fowler's sly approach.
What can this mean, that neither is in nature,
Nor in the compass of my powerful art;
That hell cannot, or else dare not speak!
Rinaldo, too, seems strangely discomposed;
What ails my love? What means that furious start?
Why do thy lovely eyes appear thus terrible?
And threatening shoot their fiery glances that way?

RINALDO: Why have you done this?

ARMIDA: What have I done? Thou art not well, my love.

RINALDO: Why have you raised these phantoms to delude me,
In that provoking posture?

ARMIDA: These phantoms are within thee, I see nothing;
I, who a hundred times a day view beings,
That are to thee invisible.
Sure, 'tis th'effect of his distempered mind;
But then my spirits who are fled unlicensed:
The more I think, the more I grow confounded.
My genius seems to whisper me within,
"Armida! Fate approaches."
An icy horror strikes through all my veins,
And freezes as it runs; not far from hence,
There is a dismal cave, the mouth of hell,

Out of the which, the old ugly beldame Night,
With twenty thousand fiends, her fearful equipage,
Each evening rushes to usurp the sky,
And in her hideous flight deform
Th'afflicted face of nature; straight, Phenissa,
Into its monstrous caverns shall descend
And thither summoning hell's blackest furies,
Fiends too abominable to behold
The face of heaven or mine,
Shall there compel them to unfold my destiny.

Ubaldo and Carlo go up to Rinaldo, who had been all this while observing them.

RINALDO: Ha! What are you,
That in this posture of defiance,
Thus dare t'explore the secrets of a solitude,
That's sacred to th'immortal powers and me?
What are you? Speak or—
CARLO: Men.
UBALDO: Soldiers.
CARLO: Friends.
UBALDO: Ubaldo.
CARLO: Carlo.
UBALDO: Now, what art thou? Look there and satisfy thyself.

[Ubaldo] presents the adamantine shield to him.

RINALDO: Damnation, what indeed? For 'tis impossible
That thou canst be Rinaldo. Oh, dishonor!
Earth open quick, and take me to the center!
Ye cedars fall and crush me to conceal me!
But what retreat can hide me from my thoughts?
For I have seen my shame, and that's to me
As much as if the assembled world beheld it.
What godlike forms are those, compared to mine?
Off ye vile trappings of soft Syrian slaves, *(tears off his garlands)*
The pride of little, base, effeminate wretches,
That want the very outside of humanity.
CARLO: Now he begins to be once more Rinaldo,
Throws off the captive, and resumes the demigod,
We come to free thee from inglorious thralldom,
Follow us.
RINALDO: Whither?
UBALDO: To Jerusalem.
RINALDO: Ha!
UBALDO: Godfrey invites thee.
CARLO: The universal camp demands thee,
Victory on her eagle's wings attends thee.
UBALDO: Fortune, and everlasting Fame expect thee.
Art thou not fired? When Europe and when Asia,
Contending for the empire of the world,
In dreadful conflict meet, is this a place;
This soft retreat, for that aspiring soul,
That once was foremost in the race of glory?
RINALDO: Great deeds are oft in solitude performed.
UBALDO: Of all created spirits, is there one
So covetous of deathless fame as thine?
Then where are the applauders here?
RINALDO: The brave can never be without applauders,
The gods, and I myself approve my actions.
UBALDO: Canst thou desert the darling cause of heaven,
And yet affirm that heaven approves thy actions?
What wants there but thy sword, O fatal warrior,
To finish this crusade with glorious victory?
T'extinguish that abominable sect,
And put an end to all their impious rites?
Break forth, and be thy godlike self once more,
The matchless champion of the Christian cause,
Who art now th'egregious champion of a woman;
Break from her influence, whose malignant aspect
Eclipses all thy glory.
RINALDO: Have neither of you seen this woman,
Whom thus disdainfully you mention?
UBALDO: Thou know'st we have.
RINALDO: Did you unmoved behold her? No, you loved her,
Even to the loss of reason, both you loved her,
Condemned and used like slaves, you doted on her;
I met you led in triumph both, and bound,
Bound in ignobler bonds than those of love;
I met you, and delivered you, unmanned
To that degree, you grumbled at your freedom,
Because your baseness had excuse no longer.
Have I a soul so little sensible,
That I should leave the soft, the kind Armida,
When her disdain and her imperious fierceness
Could so engaging prove to you?
Me she yet never gave just cause to leave her,
Unless because for me she left an empire,
And the addresses of all Asia's monarchs.
UBALDO: Our actions ought not to be rules for yours,
You have a soul of a superior order.
RINALDO: Could you persuade my vanity to that,
Great souls by mightiest passions are tormented,
Besides, Armida has ten thousand charms,
Of which you never can have any notion.
Could cruelty have binding force for you,
And am I urged to leave the last endearments
That only by their sweet remembrance pierce
My inmost soul, and rouse up sleeping raptures?
UBALDO: A hero ne'er can want a worthier mistress.
RINALDO: Thou talk'st, but ah, thou dost not think, Ubaldo.
For him who has enjoyed Armida,
There is no other mistress.
Thou hast beheld her angel form,
And frowning, it has ravished thee.
Thou know'st her science, and her wondrous wit too;
But ah, thou ne'er canst know with how much art,
She makes that wit subservient to her happiness,
When she designs to bless the man she loves,
And raise him to a god, with height of rapture.
Were you that happy man, would you forsake her?
At least thou shouldst not, Carlo.
Thy languid eyes, that glow with humid fires,
Declare too well thy soul.
CARLO: I must confess, I should not.
UBALDO: Nay, then all's lost. Heaven's darling cause is lost.
RINALDO: Ubaldo, no,

What I have said, has been designed to show,
That the great thing I now shall do is owing,
Not to the influence of your frail persuasion,
Who stand convicted both, and both confounded;
But the full force of my own reasoning virtue.
Though dearer than my life I love Armida;
I love my duty and my honor more.
And since they call, Rinaldo will obey.
But oh, thou tyrant, glory, how much gentler,
And how much lovelier in the field I found thee,
When stained with human gore, from far thou beckon'st,
And I while death and horror stalked before me,
Broke through the whole Arabian horse to join thee,
And mowed my passage through the Syrian infantry.

UBALDO: There spoke the very first, and best of heroes.

[Enter Urania.]

URANIA: *(entering)* Nay, then appear Urania.

RINALDO: The blessed Urania here!

URANIA: Yes, now you purge your stains by such contrition,
Urania dares appear,
She has with transport, and with wonder, heard thee.
Thou hast assumed a godlike resolution.

RINALDO: Yes, I will leave my very life, my soul.
Farewell thou dearer part of me, and with thee,
Pleasure farewell, a long farewell, ye raptures,
That have so often in this blissful bower,
Raised me above the height of mortal happiness.

Enter Phenissa.

PHENISSA: My lord, the queen your mistress, ha!
Bless me, what shapes are those?

URANIA: Tell her, she is no more Rinaldo's mistress,
And he no more a slave.

PHENISSA: What's this I hear? Nay then assist me hell;
Fly Nisroe, fly, and on the wings of lightning,
Convey this news I charge thee.
This certainly must turn her love to hate,
To mortal hate; and force her to destroy him.

Exit [Phenissa].

RINALDO: Now all ye separated souls of heroes,
Who in this happy isle, enjoy immortal pleasures;
Who, hovering in the balmy air around me,
Beheld the dreadful conflict in my breast,
And saw me with a bleeding heart, a victor;
Say all, if I deserve a place
In your illustrious roll.

URANIA: No Roman e'er did half so much for glory.
True, they resigned their lives for glory,
But soon their pangs were over.
Thou art contented to live greatly miserable,
But quickly let us fly, thou know'st Armida,
And know'st how far her dreadful power extends;
That power that sets earth, hell, and heaven in uproar,
While Chaos hushed, stands listening to the noise,
And wondering at confusion, not his own;
And though she should not hurt us, she may shake us.
But hark, already she begins, already,
Hell's grizzly tyrant takes the dire alarm

The serpent and basses [play] softly under the stage.

In frantic haste even now the furies arm,
Th'infernal trumpet through the abyss profound,
Horribly rumbles with its dreary sound.
Hark!

Here the music plays out.

In that roar hell's dreadful mounds it passed.
Hark!

Here the alarm plays out again.

Now the vaulted heavens restore the dismal blast.

UBALDO: I stiffen with astonishment,

CARLO: And I grow chill with horror.
Bless me, what hideous forms are those,
That threatening nod their ghastly skulls,
And stalk t'oppose our passage.

RINALDO: Why? Those are creatures whom their crimes have thrown
So far below us, we to them are gods
In scorn of all their empty threats I'll own.
Are we not spirits too? Immortal beings,
Whom only we ourselves have power to hurt?

[The] Alarm [sounds] again.

I fear the fair Armida's softness more
Than all these ghastly shapes, and all this dreadful roar.

[Exeunt all.]

The end of the third act.

In the music between this and the fourth act, the instruments express the [foresaid] alarm that the Infernal Regions take at Rinaldo's departure.

Act 4

Scene: The country before the enchanted palaces.

Enter Phenissa and Nisroe.

NISROE: Why am I called with so much eager haste?

PHENISSA: Oh, I want time to tell thee, haste, be gone,
Fly, fly this very moment,
Swift as a storm, impetuous as the lightning,
To execute Armida's dreadful will.

NISROE: Rinaldo—

PHENISSA: Is gone, with vengeance, and with death o'ertake him;
Go, bid th'avenging ministers of fate
Rush through the inmost chambers of the earth,
And shake the world's foundations.
Bid the tempestuous powers that rule the air
Let loose th'unbridled fury of the winds,
To overthrow their empire.
And let the furies with infernal horrors
Affright, astonish and confound the traitor.
What! Stand'st thou pausing now the Queen's betrayed?

NISROE: I do not pause, this moment thou'rt obeyed.
Behold that grisly form which there ascends,

Spirits ascend.

The dire forerunner of confusion;
As in this western main a small black cloud
Lifting its threatening head above the horizon.
The signal of the warring winds

Foreruns the dreadful hurricane—
This rising phantom by its black appearance
Alarms millions of immortal spirits,
To raise up tumults that will shake all nature.

PHENISSA: Let us be gone then, thou to hell,
And to the Queen, my mistress, I,
To tell her what thou hast done.
Exeunt [Nisroe and Phenissa].

Musical Entertainment No. 5

[Sung] by Spirits, that come to revenge the injury that Rinaldo is thought by them to have done to Armida.

8
Vn. 1
Vn. 2
Va.
B.c.
12
soft
[soft]
Spirit
Ye spir- its that dwell in earth, fi- re, and air, Hith-er, hith-er, hith-er, hur-ry, hur-ry, hur-ry,
16
loud
[loud]
hur- ry, hur- ry, hur- ry, hur- ry- ing re- pair; Be- hold your great mis- tress, Ar-

19
Vn. 1
Vn. 2
Va.
Spirit
-mi- da's be- trayed, Hith- er, hith- er, hith- er, hur- ry, hur- ry, hur- ry, hith- er, hith- er, hith- er, hur- ry, hur- ry, hur- ry
B.c.
22
Vn. 1
Vn. 2
Va.
Spirit
all to her aid, Hith- er, hith- er, hith- er, hur- ry, hur- ry, hur- ry, hith- er, hith- er, hith- er, hur- ry, hur- ry, hur- ry
B.c.
25
Vn. 1
Vn. 2
Va.
Spirit
all to her aid.
B.c.

29
Chorus
Vn. 1
Vn. 2
Va.
S
Lo, lo, lo, from earth, lo, from earth, from
A
Lo, lo, lo, from earth, lo, from earth, from
SPIRITS
T
Lo, lo, lo, from earth, lo, from earth, from
B
Lo, lo, lo, from earth, lo, from earth, from
[6]
B.c.
32
Vn. 1
Vn. 2
Va.
S
hell, and from sky, With ven- geance, with ven- geance, with
A
hell, and from sky, With ven- geance, with ven- geance, with ven- geance, with ven- geance, with
SPIRITS
T
hell, and from sky, With ven- geance, with ven- geance, with ven- geance, with ven- geance, with
B
hell, and from sky, With ven- - geance, with ven-
[5]
B.c.

35
Vn. 1
Vn. 2
Va.
S
ven- geance lad- en we fly, we fly, With ven-
A
ven- geance lad- en we fly, we fly, we fly, we fly, With
SPIRITS
T
ven- geance lad- en we fly, we fly, with ven- geance we fly, With
B
- geance lad- en we fly, we fly, With
B.c.
[♮3]
38
Vn. 1
Vn. 2
Va.
S
- - geance lad- en we fly, With ven-
A
ven- geance, with ven- geance, with ven- geance, with ven- geance lad- en we fly, With ven- geance, with ven- geance, with
SPIRITS
T
ven- geance, with ven- geance, with ven- geance, with ven- geance lad- en we fly, With [ven- geance, with ven- geance, with
B
ven- - geance lad- en we fly, With ven-
B.c.
7 [4] 6 5 4 3 7 [4] 6

42
Vn. 1
Vn. 2
Va.
S
- geance lad- en we fly.
A
ven- geance, with ven- geance lad- en we fly.
SPIRITS
T
ven- geance, with ven- geance] lad- en we fly.
B
- geance lad- en we fly.
B.c.

(45)
Vn. 1
soft
Vn. 2
[soft]
Va.
[soft]
Spirit
Ye fiends that are lurk- ing in graves, Or glid- ing in vault- ed caves, All work- ing a- main in your holes,
B.c.
[soft]

49
Vn. 1
Vn. 2
Va.
Spirit
Heave, heave up the crum- bling earth like moles, Till the moun- tain
B.c.
52
shakes, Till the moun-tain shakes, Till the moun-tain shakes, And the rock its ba- sis for- sakes, And the heart of the trai- tor
55
loud
[loud]
quakes,
And the heart of the trai-tor quakes,
[loud]

58
Vn. 1
Vn. 2
Va.
Spirit
B.c.
soft
[soft]
[soft]
Till the moun-tain shakes, And the rock its ba- sis for- sakes, And the heart of the trai- tor
♮3
4
3
[soft]
61
quakes,
And the heart of the trai-tor quakes, And the
7
[4]
6
5
64
[Chorus]
heart of the trai- tor quakes.
S
A
T
B
SPIRITS
'Tis done, 'tis done, 'tis
'Tis done, 'tis done, 'tis
'Tis done, 'tis done, 'tis
'Tis done, 'tis done, 'tis
[6]

67
Vn. 1
Vn. 2
Va.
S
done, see, see, the moun-tain shakes, the moun- tain shakes, see, see, see,
A
done, see, see, the moun-tain shakes, see, see, see, see, see, see, see, see, the moun- tain
T
done, see, see, the moun-tain shakes, see, see, see, see, see, see, see, see, the moun- tain
B
done, see, see, the moun-tain shakes, the moun- tain shakes, the moun- tain shakes,
SPIRITS
B.c.
70
Spirit
Ye
S
see, the moun- tain shakes, And the heart of the trai- tor quakes, the heart of the trai- tor quakes.
A
shakes, the moun- tain shakes, And the heart of the trai- tor quakes, the heart of the trai- tor quakes.
T
shakes, the moun- tain shakes, And the heart of the trai- tor quakes, the heart of the trai- tor quakes.
B
And the heart of the trai- tor quakes, the heart of the trai- tor quakes.

73
Vn. 1
Vn. 2
Va.
Spirit
B.c.
soft
[soft]
[soft]
[soft]
powers who gov- ern the air, Let nought but con- fu- sion be there; Haste to send
77
forth The storm- y north, Haste to send forth The storm- y
83
north, And un- bind the deep mouth Of the blus- ter-ing south: Let 'em

89
Vn. 1
Vn. 2
Va.
Spirit
blow, let 'em blow, let 'em blow, let 'em blow, let 'em
B.c.
[5]
95
blow, let 'em blow, till with fu- ry they roar,
[3]
[6]
6
6
101
And am- bi- tious old O- cean dis- dains the
5
[3]
[6]

107
Vn. 1
Vn. 2
Va.
Spirit
shore, Let 'em blow, let 'em blow, till with fu- ry they
B.c.
[6] ♮3 [♮3]
113
Vn. 1
Vn. 2
Va.
Spirit
roar, And am- bi- tious old O- cean dis- dains the shore,
B.c.
♯3 [6] [♯6] ♯3

119
[Chorus]
Vn. 1
Vn. 2
Va.
Spirit
And am- bi- tious old O- cean dis- dains the shore.
S
Hark!
SPIRITS
A
Hark!
T
Hark!
B
Hark!
B. Vn.
B.c.
♯3
125
Vn. 1
Vn. 2
Va.
S
Hark! Hark how they blow! Hark!
SPIRITS
A
Hark! Hark how they blow! Hark!
T
Hark! Hark how they blow! Hark!
B
Hark! Hark how they blow! Hark!
B. Vn.
B.c.
♯3
♮3

129
Vn. 1
Vn. 2
Va.
S
Hark! Hark how they blow! Hark!
A
Hark! Hark how they blow! Hark, hark!
T
Hark! Hark how they blow! Hark, hark!
B
Hark! Hark how they blow! Hark!
SPIRITS
B. Vn.
B.c.
[6] ♮3
133
Vn. 1
Vn. 2
Va.
S
Hark! Hark how they blow! Hark! Hark,
A
Hark! Hark how they blow! Hark! Hark,
T
Hark! Hark how they blow! Hark! Hark,
B
Hark! Hark how they blow! Hark! Hark,
SPIRITS
B. Vn.
B.c.
♮3 [6] 6

137
Vn. 1
Vn. 2
Va.
S
hark! Hark, hark how they blow! If they go
A
hark! Hark, hark how they blow! If they go
SPIRITS
T
hark! Hark, hark how they blow! If they go
B
hark! Hark, hark how they blow! If they go
B. Vn.
♯3 [6] ♯3 ♮3
B.c.
141
Vn. 1
Vn. 2
Va.
S
on, through the void they will sweep The heavens, the
A
on, through the void they will sweep The heavens, the
SPIRITS
T
on, through the void they will sweep The heavens, the
B
on, through the void they will sweep The heavens, the
B. Vn.
♯3 ♯4 2 [♯6]
B.c.

145
Vn. 1
Vn. 2
Va.
SPIRITS
S
earth, and the deep, If they go on, through the
A
earth, and the deep, If they go on, through the
T
earth, and the deep, If they go on, through the
B
earth, and the deep, If they go on, through the
B. Vn.
B.c.
♯3 [♯3]
149
Vn. 1
Vn. 2
Va.
SPIRITS
S
void they will sweep The heav- ens, the earth, and the
A
void they will sweep The heav- ens, the earth, and the
T
void they will sweep The heav- ens, the earth, and the
B
void they will sweep The heav- ens, the earth, and the
B. Vn.
B.c.
6 7 [6 4]

153
Vn. 1
Vn. 2
Va.
SPIRITS
S
deep, And the world in- to cha- os will throw, And the
A
deep, And the world in- to cha- os will throw, And the
T
deep, And the world in- to cha- os will throw, And the
B
deep, And the world in- to cha- os will throw, And the
B. Vn.
B.c.
[6 4]
♯3
157
Vn. 1
Vn. 2
Va.
SPIRITS
S
world in- to cha- os will throw, And the world in- to
A
world in- to cha- os will throw, And the world in- to
T
world in- to cha- os will throw, And the world in- to
B
world in- to cha- os will throw, And the world in- to
B. Vn.
B.c.
[♯6]
♯3
♯3
[6 4]

161
Vn. 1
Vn. 2
Va.
SPIRITS
S
chaos will throw, And the world into chaos will
A
chaos will throw, And the world into chaos will
T
chaos will throw, And the world into chaos will
B
chaos will throw, And the world into chaos will
B. Vn.
B.c.
♯3
♯6
♯3
165
[soft]
throw!
throw!
throw!
throw!
♯3
[6]

169
Vn. 1
Vn. 2
Va.
Spirit
Now fly- ing in crowds, Charge, charge all your clouds, Charge 'em all with de- struc- tive
B.c.
173
thun- der, Let it roar till it rents the vast all a- sun- der. Let the
♮3 [6] 4 ♮3
177
light- ning fear- ful- ly blaze, Till mor- tals who gaze, Till mor- tals who gaze, Fall
4
2
6
5

182
Vn. 1
Vn. 2
Va.
Spirit
dead, fall dead, fall dead, fall dead at the ter- ri- ble won- der,
B.c.
6 6 [6] 4 [5] 3
188
Vn. 1
Vn. 2
Va.
Spirit
Till mor- tals who gaze, Fall dead, fall dead at the ter- ri- ble
B.c.
6 6 6 4 3
194
(thunder)
Play all
Vn. 1
[Play all]
Vn. 2
[Play all]
Va.
Spirit
won- der.
B. Vn.
B.c.

198
Vn. 1
Vn. 2
Va.
B. Vn.
B.c.
202
6
206
[Chorus]
S
A
T
B
SPIRITS
'Tis done, 'tis done, 'tis done, 'tis done, 'tis done, 'tis done, and we
4 3

210
Vn. 1
Vn. 2
Va.
SPIRITS
S
A
T
B
1.
shake, and we shake At the dire, the dire con- fu- sion we make, At the
B.c.
214
2.
Spirit
Ye fu- ries who reign in un- quench- a- ble fires, To the
fu- sion we make.
soft
[soft]

218
Vn. 1
Vn. 2
Va.
Spirit
sound of your yells tune your hor- ri- ble lyres; And give us that mu- sic by which you re- dou- ble The
B.c.
222
Play all
[Play all]
[Play all]
hor- rors of hell, the hor- rors of hell and un- speak- a- ble trou- ble.
226
Chorus
S
A
T
B
SPIRITS
'Tis
'Tis
'Tis
'Tis

231
Vn. 1
Vn. 2
Va.
Spirit
Now add to the sym- pho- ny clink- ing of chains.
S
done, 'tis done.
A
done, 'tis done.
SPIRITS
T
done, 'tis done.
B
done, 'tis done.
[♭3] ♯3 6 5
B.c.
234
Vn. 1
Vn. 2
Va.
Spirit
Add the howls of the
S
'Tis done, 'tis done.
A
'Tis done, 'tis done.
SPIRITS
T
'Tis done, 'tis done.
B
'Tis done, 'tis done.
♮3 6 5 ♮3 [♮3]
B.c.

237
Vn. 1
Vn. 2
Va.
Spirit
damned, in the height of their pains.
Add their screams and their
(Howl here and then chorus)
S
Oh! 'Tis done, 'Tis done.
A
Oh! 'Tis done, 'Tis done.
SPIRITS
T
Oh! 'Tis done, 'Tis done.
B
Oh! 'Tis done, 'Tis done.
B.c.

241
Vn. 1
Vn. 2
Va.
Spirit
roar, and their ser-pen-tine hiss.
Let Lu- ci- fer's
(Here they scream, roar and hiss, and then chorus)
S
'Tis done, 'tis done.
A
'Tis done, 'tis done.
SPIRITS
T
'Tis done, 'tis done.
B
'Tis done, 'tis done.
B.c.
♮3 ♮3

245
Vn. 1
Vn. 2
Va.
Spirit
B. Vn.
B.c.
Play all
[Play all]
[Play all]
thun-der now an-swer to this, And bel- low al- ter- nate- ly through the a- byss.
248
Vn. 1
Vn. 2
Va.
B. Vn.
B.c.
252
Vn. 1
Vn. 2
Va.
B. Vn.
B.c.

256
(Thunder)
Vn. 1
Vn. 2
Va.
B. Vn.
B.c.
260
264
(Thunder)

268
Vn. 1
Vn. 2
Va.
B. Vn.
♮3
B.c.
♮3
272
Vn. 1
Vn. 2
Va.
S
'Tis
A
'Tis
SPIRITS
T
'Tis
B
'Tis
B. Vn.
♮5
B.c.
♮3
[♮3]

276
(Thunder)
Vn. 1
Vn. 2
Va.
S
done, 'tis done, 'tis done, and 'tis past our
A
done, 'tis done, 'tis done, and 'tis past our
SPIRITS
T
done, 'tis done, 'tis done, and 'tis past our
B
done, 'tis done, 'tis done, and 'tis past our
B.c.
[♮3]
♮3
280
Vn. 1
Vn. 2
Va.
S
pow- er to know, Whith- er this be Cha- os or
A
pow- er to know, Whith- er this be Cha- os or
SPIRITS
T
pow- er to know, Whith- er this be Cha- os or
B
pow- er to know, Whith- er this be Cha- os or
B.c.
[6]

284
Vn. 1
Vn. 2
Va.
SPIRITS
S
A
T
B
no, Whith- er this be Cha- os or no, and 'tis
B.c.
♮3
[♮3]
[6]
288
past our pow- er to know, Whith- er this be
[6]
♮3

292
Vn. 1
Vn. 2
Va.
S
Cha- os or no, Whith- er this be Cha- os or
A
Cha- os or no, Whith- er this be Cha- os or
SPIRITS
T
Cha- os or no, Whith- er this be Cha- os or
B
Cha- os or no, Whith- er this be Cha- os or
B.c.
♮3 [6] [6] ♮3

296
Vn. 1
Vn. 2
Va.
S
no?
A
no?
SPIRITS
T
no?
B
no?
B.c.
6 7 6 7 6 ♮3

Enter Armida and Phenissa.

PHENISSA: At length you have moved his mighty soul.
ARMIDA: But 'tis with anger, not with fear, he's moved,
See where transported with a noble fury,
Lovelily dreadful as a warring angel,
He drives the infernal phantoms all before him.
PHENISSA: Redouble your efforts.
ARMIDA: That certainly destroys him.
PHENISSA: No matter, since you cannot shake him, crush him.
ARMIDA: Thus godlike! Thus insensible of fear!
PHENISSA: Think he's insensible of love too.
ARMIDA: Perhaps he may relent. He comes this way,
And I will make the trial.
PHENISSA: Relent! What can you hope? What can you do?
When furies can't prevail?
ARMIDA: Show him a greater.
PHENISSA: A greater? What greater?
ARMIDA: A woman,
An injured woman!
Wronged in her love, and raging for revenge.
PHENISSA: Be wise, and let him perish.
ARMIDA: Yes, he shall perish if he dares persist;
But thou the giver of bold fatal counsels,
Assure thyself that thou shalt perish with him.
But see, he comes, and to my wish alone,
Divided by the tempest from his friends,
Without reply be gone.

Exit Phenissa.

Enter Rinaldo; thunder and lightning, and horrid music [occur] alternately.

ARMIDA: Be still, at my command be still, ye furies,
And ye, restrain your roaring mouths, ye thunders,
For I am to be heard.
RINALDO: Ha! The Queen!
The only object which I would avoid!
Ay, here's the sight at which my genius shrinks,
Now, all ye motives to my great proceeding,
Thou the remembrance of my former triumphs,
And thou the hope of future, thou, O glory,
That day and night in my aspiring mind
Ragest with inextinguishable fire;
United aid me in this dreadful conflict,
And thou, too conscious of the great original,
Rouse, rouse each nobler faculty, my soul,
Exert thy utmost force in thy defense,
For dreadful is the danger.
Armida!
ARMIDA: Traitor!
RINALDO: Traitor!
Armida has had kinder thoughts of me.
ARMIDA: Ungrateful wretch! Am I at last reproached with it?
I have, and therefore doubly thou'rt a traitor.
Have I selected thee from all mankind,
To heap upon thee obligations?
And basely after all to steal away?
RINALDO: You wrong me.
Are not your sentinels in every corner?
Have not your airy scouts o'er spread the island?
How could I hope then to depart unknown?
ARMIDA: Confusion? Am I then defied? Hark!
Th'impatient thunder grumbles to be at thee;
Ten thousand raging fiends around thee wait,
Watching the sign to spring and to devour thee,
At my least nod most certain death attends thee.
RINALDO: I go to seek him in the search of glory,
And if I find him here,
There's a long voyage saved.
ARMIDA: Then you will go?
RINALDO: Will! Have you not urged it?
ARMIDA: Oh, confusion! What do I hear?
Audacious fool to tempt thy certain ruin,
And basely to presume to that degree
Upon the poor remains of tenderness,
Which to this moment have preserved thee,
I urged it?
RINALDO: Yes, urged it by your impotent attempts,
To fright me from departure.
ARMIDA: Oh, patience yet a moment!
RINALDO: The greatness of my mind is now concerned,
And though I had no other call than that,
I would be gone. Gods! That you should descend
So far beneath yourself
To think that you could love a man so base,
As to be swayed by fear.
ARMIDA: By my remaining hopes of great revenge,
I ne'er designed to fright thee, but destroy thee;
I know thy soul incapable of fear,
Even of the fear of doing basest wrongs.
RINALDO: Whom have I wronged?
ARMIDA: Whom hast thou sworn eternally to love?
RINALDO: Armida! And that hour I cease to love her,
Hear me, ye gods! Pierce me with all your bolts;
But from this hour I will ne'er see her more.
ARMIDA: Hell and confusion! Dar'st thou mock my misery?
RINALDO: I dare not do a thing so much beneath
The greatness of my soul.
ARMIDA: Did'st thou not say that thou resolv'st to love me?
RINALDO: Eternally.
ARMIDA: And yet resolv'st to leave me?
RINALDO: By heavens, forever.
ARMIDA: O vile dissembler!
RINALDO: Madam, I must be gone, for I am called
With such a voice as man dares not resist.
ARMIDA: By whom?
RINALDO: By Victory, by Fame, by heaven.
ARMIDA: To do a barbarous thing? Impossible!
RINALDO: 'Twas but this moment that th'immortal powers,
Called loudly from above "Begone Rinaldo,
Without delay, begone; 'tis we command thee;
Fortune, and Victory, and Fame attend thee;
This very night begone or stay forever."
ARMIDA: Mere vapor! And deluding vision all!
RINALDO: 'Tis real all by heaven, this very moment
I heard th'ethereal trump upon the mountain,

While the hill trembled with th'eternal clangor;
Urania too, and Carlo and Ubaldo
With messages from Godfrey are arrived.
ARMIDA: They must return.
RINALDO: Without me?
ARMIDA: Fate has by me pronounced it.
RINALDO: What will th'army? What will all Asia think?
ARMIDA: The greatest and most glorious of them all,
Will envy thy transcendent happiness.
RINALDO: But envy always stirs up base-born minds,
To blacken whom they envy.
I shall become the common talk of slaves.
ARMIDA: They can but talk, while in revenge we'll live.
RINALDO: Nay, then I leave you as my mortal enemy.
ARMIDA: Your mortal enemy? Provoking wretch!
On every side avoidless fate surrounds thee.
To whom then doest thou owe the very breath,
That thus pronounces this audacious insolence?
Is it thy mortal enemy preserves thee?
RINALDO: Yes, 'tis my mortal enemy who e'er
Preserves me from a glorious death,
To see me live a cursed life with infamy,
Think of my purple rivals of the East.
What will they say? That they were all disdained for—
Gods! I want patience to support the thoughts of it.
But if no sense of my dishonor moves thee,
Think of thy own; what will they say of thee?
That you so far beneath yourself descended,
To give a wretch possession of your soul,
Who vilely could renounce eternal fame,
To squander an inglorious life away
In a fond woman's arms.
If thou so little art concerned for me,
I, who love thee beyond all bounds, must leave thee,
To vindicate thy fame from bold blasphemers;
And carrying terror to the very courts
Of my imperial rivals, make them know
That he alone was worthy of thy choice,
Who had the power when duty called to leave thee.
Oh! Wouldst but thou Armida do thy part,
And show by bearing this departure greatly,
That she of all her sex was worthy me;
Who in the furious height of all her love,
To glory could resign me.
ARMIDA: Ay, here's another cause for my detaining thee,
My fame as well as love requires thy stay;
What would those monarchs say shouldst thou desert me?
How would they scorn the weakness of my choice,
Or meanness of my beauty?
RINALDO: Then to secure that fame lo here I swear,
The memory of what has passed between us
Shall in this corner of the world lie buried:
In Europe and in Asia unrecorded:
And that of all the actions of my life,
Alone shall be forgotten.
ARMIDA: Me wouldst thou have give faith to thy false oaths?
The very breath that swears, declares thee perjured?
Am I to be forgot, as well as left?
RINALDO: You mistake me.
ARMIDA: Fate ne'er mistakes, and traitor is at hand.

Thunder [sounds] and spirits approach.

RINALDO: I thank thee; since for glorious death I leave thee,
How could I ever hope to fall more greatly,
Than dauntless, in this dreadful wrack of nature?
ARMIDA: So brave! His greatness shakes my soul, he frowns
With congregated clouds about his brows,
As if he were the god who threw these thunders;
And he commanded nature.
Yes, thou shalt die, but not with so much pleasure
As fondly thou believ'st, for thou shalt die
Convicted, and remorse shall plague that soul
Which fear of danger never could disturb.
Canst thou thyself believe thou art not perjured?
RINALDO: Perjured?
ARMIDA: Yes, perjured!
Hast thou not sworn eternally to love me?
RINALDO: Well!
ARMIDA: And yet hast sworn to leave me too forever?
RINALDO: That is to say, I love thee with a passion
That hopeless and in absence will endure.
ARMIDA: But thou art called, alas! And by whom called?
By Victory, by Fame, by heaven; fine visions!
By thy satiety thou'rt called, false man,
By the base lightness of thy changing temper.
RINALDO: You wrong me.
ARMIDA: I do not; had heaven enjoined thee to depart,
Would it command thee to appear inhuman;
Sprung from a rock and by a tigress nursed?
For hast thou, say, fetched one reluctant groan?
Have not thy unrelenting eyes been dry,
Yet seen my poor distracted heart weep blood?
Hast thou so much as cast one pitying glance,
On my hard fortune? On my fortune said I?
My dreadful fate, my everlasting ruin,
And canst thou falsely then affirm thou lovest?
Doest thou not now convicted fall a traitor?
Be gone, and meet the fate which there attends thee.
RINALDO: Farewell.
ARMIDA: What have I done? He goes to certain death.
Stay; hast thou not one word t'excuse thy crime?
RINALDO: Yes, yes, 'tis in my power to justify myself,
To your confusion too, of that be certain.
ARMIDA: Do it then.
RINALDO: No.
ARMIDA: You must.
RINALDO: I'll die a thousand deaths first.
ARMIDA: *(aside)* By heavens, I feel I am a very woman.
Rinaldo, if ever I was dear to thee;
If ere I gave thee high and perfect pleasure,
Here by its dear remembrance I conjure thee,
That thou wouldst satisfy this last request,

Let me but know thou art not false,
And I shall die with pleasure.
RINALDO: Oh, urge it not, if ere thou lov'st Rinaldo.
ARMIDA: Why?
RINALDO: In pity to us both.
ARMIDA: Ha! Now by heaven I long, I die to know it.
RINALDO: Yet, if thou lov'st Rinaldo, let it die with me,
Thou hast, alas, endured too much already!
Why shouldst thou strive to know a thing which known,
Will break thy wretched heart?
ARMIDA: To break my heart you must continue silent,
If I persist to think thee false, I die;
Then speak and let me live.
RINALDO: Thou hast o'ercome, but dread the fatal consequence,
Here I relax the violent effort
Which has thus far suppressed the struggling passion,
That tore my very vitals to get free,
I told thee that I loved thee, my Armida,
I told thee not how far, that thou shalt see;
Then with those eyes that through the stars see fate,
Look upon mine and through them view my soul;
Say, do I love thee now, art thou yet satisfied?
ARMIDA: Prodigious alteration in a moment!
Thou doest not only love, but thou art love;
Come to my heart, and feel it leap to meet thee.
RINALDO: Why wouldst thou urge me to this fatal weakness
That has undone us both? And why return it
With that bewitching softness, which afresh
Must plunge me in the torments of the damned?
Why wouldst thou sharpen thus the cruel sting
Of that severe necessity, which now

[Rinaldo] breaks [away] from her.

O cursed hour, eternally divides us?
ARMIDA: Ah gods! Ah wretch! Ah curst, perfidious wretch!
Blast him ye lightnings, and ye furies tear him;
The traitor has dissembled tenderness,
To torture me the more.
RINALDO: Now, now, O all ye heavenly powers, defend me.
In this first dreadful moment of my life,
Not from the danger of her potent art,
But from myself, y'eternal powers, defend me!
ARMIDA: Now, now, Tartarean deities, revenge me,
But hold, what fury want I but my own;
Mine is the wrong, the vengeance shall be mine:
Die, traitor.

[Armida] holds up her dagger.

RINALDO: *(presenting his breast)* Do strike and pierce thy image here, so fixed,
That nothing but a dagger can remove it.
ARMIDA: What has he said? And canst thou pierce him now?
I can, for his is a perfidious tongue,
But then his eyes, his lovesick eyes, speak truth;
I cannot hurt him with that melting look:
Love in his eyes defends him. Curse on thy tenderness,
Then pierce thyself, then stab him here.

[Armida] stabs herself.

RINALDO: Oh, heavens!
What hast thou done? The dagger's in thy bosom.
ARMIDA: Could I oblige thee more?
Now I prevent thy barbarous design;
This was the only way, I had to abandon thee.
RINALDO: I have a soul that loves and dares like yours,
And thus.
ARMIDA: Ah hold, Rinaldo, hold, if I am dear to thee,
By that dear love I here conjure thee hold!
Throw down that cursed instrument of death,
I can with constancy support my wound;
I die to think of thine.
RINALDO: Ho, there, Phenissa, help Ubaldo, Carlo?
ARMIDA: Alas! Thou call'st in vain, I die, Rinaldo.
RINALDO: What will become of me? Thou bleedst to death,
And yet no succors nigh.
Let me support thy lovely fainting limbs,
Back to the palace where Phenissa waits thee;
Now where's ambition?
ARMIDA: If I would live, I want no mortal aid;
A thousand powerful spirits round me wait,
Hark! How they groaning all deplore my fate!
Hark! How their lyres resound a rueful strain,
Which shows them sensible of all my pain.
RINALDO: O grief! O infinite excess of woe!
That makes the very damned with piercing moan
Lament our sorrows, and forget their own.

The end of the fourth act.

In the Music between this and the fifth act, the Spirits attending on Armida, express their grief for the calamity which has befallen her.

Act 5

Enter Rinaldo, Armida, Phenissa.

RINALDO: Now you and heaven have perfected my joy,
And all I would have asked prevented:
Thou hast renounced thy faith, renounced thy art,
And thy wound is not mortal; my friends too,
My friends will all be ravished, I'll but seek them,
And with them in a moment I'll return.
ARMIDA: Wilt thou begone then?
RINALDO: I must, it is in order to our happiness.
ARMIDA: I know it, for yet methinks 'tis death to part with thee?
RINALDO: It is but for a moment.
ARMIDA: But yet that moment sure will break my heart.
How dolefully it beats with dying blows?
As if with thee my very soul departed.
How would eternal separation plague me?
But see, Rinaldo, there; look here, Phenissa!

What mean these winged ill omens of the air
That passing brush me with their deadly pinions,
And seem the forlorn hope of fate?
Rinaldo: I see nothing.
Phenissa: Nor I.
Armida: Is it possible? Nor hear you any voice?
Rinaldo: None but that voice whose music charms my soul.
Armida: Nor you?
Phenissa: Nor I.
Armida: Hark! How it cries again, "Prepare Armida,
Dispatch, we're grown impotent of delay:
See, where we all stand ready to receive thee,
Assembled in the air, we hovering stand,
And instantly expect thee."
Rinaldo: What do I hear? Her mind is much disturbed,
And danger's imminent, I must be swift,
On wings of fear which thou hast lent I'll fly,
And in a moment with my friends return.
Phenissa: *(just as he goes out)* My lord.
Armida: What want you?
Phenissa: Madam, I thought my lord Rinaldo called.
Armida: Sure so he did, for see he turns this way,
And seems to beckon to you.
Fly, to know what he wants.
She goes after him to the door.
Rinaldo: Wants the Queen anything, Phenissa?
Phenissa: No my lord!
Rinaldo: Why am I called then?
Phenissa: My lord,
I have something of importance to impart to you,
Which the Queen must not hear.
Rinaldo: I am now in haste, my impatient friends expect me,
I'll instantly return.
Exit [Rinaldo].
Phenissa: You will! Why then the sun, that all things sees,
Sees not a wretch that's so forlorn, as I am:
Return? For what? To bear the queen to Palestine?
Whither must I transport myself? To Syria?
Without Armida? Or to Godfrey's army?
Thou! Thou the mortal foe to their religion!
But such Armida was! Renounce thy faith!
Thou hast a queen's example!
Suppose I should? Alas! I have an art,
An art, which Christians utterly abhor,
And that I never, never can renounce:
Her, all th'infernal powers obeyed, attracted
By supreme knowledge and by sovereign beauty!
For in her face, they saw the bright reflection
Of that refulgent place, from which they fell,
But I, alas! O dire remembrance! I
Am by indissoluble contract bound.
This voyage I must then obstruct or perish!
Then his return I must obstruct or perish:
But the black stratagem that Fate suggests,
Perhaps may touch Armida's precious life:
No, by discovery of the truth at last
I can prevent that dire calamity.—
Armida: What says Rinaldo?
Phenissa: What said your doleful heart at his departure?
What said the winged ill omens of the air?
And what the voices of the eternal beings?
Hear them once more! Ye spirits now assist me.
[Phenissa] waves her wand. [A] Spirit rises and sings.

[Spirit] sinks.

PHENISSA: What say they now?
ARMIDA: Gods, I am tortured, I am stung to madness!
(aside) Let 'em say what they will: I'll not believe 'em.
PHENISSA: Will you give credit to Rinaldo then?
Since you must know what he himself has said.
ARMIDA: Ah gods, and was it that?
PHENISSA: And was it that? What could it be but that?
Or what could he declare but that
Which you were not to hear:
He coldly bade me comfort you.
ARMIDA: Ah! Comfort from a devil! But be hushed!
(aside) Be hushed my soul but only for this moment:
And be as mad as all the winds the next.

And ye, ye tyrant gods, unless y'are pleased
To see perfidiousness pass unrevenged:
While thus you plague the creature of your hands,
Only for too much truth; for too much love;
Assist my enfeebled arm this once, and then
Hurl all your thunders at my wretched head,
And take your willing victim.

PHENISSA: So, she resents it greatly.
I see a noble fury in her eyes.

ARMIDA: Why then Rinaldo's gone?

PHENISSA: Most certainly.

ARMIDA: Confusion! I must now make haste:
I shall be mad too soon else.
But how durst you, my slave, conceal his treason?
How did you dare t'abet his damned design?

PHENISSA: To abet it!

ARMIDA: Ay, how did you dare t'abet it?

PHENISSA: Hell had suggested—

ARMIDA: What?

PHENISSA: Why, that you—

ARMIDA: Die, and consult it better.

[Armida] stabs Phenissa. She dies.

So, 'twas exactly leveled at thy heart:
Would I had always taken aim as justly.
And hast thou then forsaken me? What, me?
Me, couldst thou then forsake? Is't possible?
Me, that had laid out all my soul upon thee?
That willingly, that gladly would have died for thee!
And couldst thou not be satisfied, unless
Thou murder'st me thyself? O wretched man!
Can you see this, you gods, and not revenge it?
Revenge it then, revenge it then, ye devils!
Who with abhorrency and detestation
Foretold this more than devilish act!
They hear thee not! My spirits too have left me.
But behold!
Phenissa there lies dead! Rinaldo's gone.
Whither must I go? Ha! Where am I left?
Thrice has yon planet waned and thrice increased,
Since I came flying to these Isles of Fortune:
In all which time no footstep has appeared
Of any human creature here inhabiting:
Nor has one sail been seen to dare the winds!
Upon this unknown ocean! But this morning
I seemed to be the darling care of heaven!
The powerfulest queen of all the Eastern world!
The adoration of mankind: O dreadful change!
But have I not one friend in heaven or hell?
Yes, one I have: then let him come! Come death!
Come thou most generous of th'immortal powers!
The only god that's true to th'unhappy:
Thus let me guide thee to my faithful heart.
Take heed, how thou a second time mistakest!
Ah gods! Thou hast a second time mistaken!
And I have now not strength enough t'assist thee!
Yet hast thou done thy work! And though thy hand
Is slow, I find 'tis sure.

A noise [sounds from] without.

What's that, a noise?
The trampling sure of feet, which this way tend!
Oh, all ye powers, the Christians are returning!
Is it my weakness that deludes my eyes,
Or has the barb'rous man relented? Ha!
He has, he has! Oh, all ye eternal powers!
What have I done? Now death forbear a moment!
That with my dying breath I may upbraid him,
That with my dying breath I may forgive him,
And that my soul may blessing him, expire.

Enter Rinaldo, Urania, Ubaldo, Carlo.

URANIA: Not far from hence you know you left Armida!

The stage is darkened.

RINALDO: A very little further on the right:
Upon a sudden 'tis exceeding dark.

URANIA: Yes, with a darkness foreign to the place:
A fog, that steaming from the mouth of hell,
Doubles the native horrors of the night:
Be cautious! Cautious, how thou treadst, Rinaldo;
Lest blindly guided by thy headstrong love
Thou stumblest on despair!
Whom left you with Armida?

RINALDO: Phenissa.

URANIA: Armida's evil genius bore that name,
The source of all her woes.

ARMIDA: O cursed Phenissa! Hast thou then betrayed me?
Is't possible?

CARLO: Angels, and all ye host of heaven defend me.
(stumbling on Phenissa) What dismal shape is this?

URANIA: The remnant of the wretch that was Phenissa.

RINALDO: Look down upon me, ye eternal powers!
Phenissa! Where? Oh where?

URANIA: Where? Here! Look here, Rinaldo,
Now see thou show'st thyself a man! A man!
That's not enough. Be what thou art, a hero!
And then with steadfast eyes, and heart unshaken,
Behold ill fate lie there.

RINALDO: Oh! Oh!
Not man nor hero can ill fate resist,
And thus it tears me down: all conquering death,
Thou art indeed the grisly king of terrors!

UBALDO: Son of Bertoldo! Be thyself this moment.

CARLO: Think of thy glory!

UBALDO: Think of past trophies and of future triumphs!

CARLO: Think that the army of the East surveys thee!

URANIA: Think that a thousand demigods surround thee.

RINALDO: O my Armida.

ARMIDA: And art thou come, my hero? Art thou mine?
Take, take my fleeting life, ye envious powers!
For life with thee exceeded mortal happiness.

RINALDO: What wrought this dreadful work of fate?

URANIA: Leave that discovery to me, Rinaldo!
For know that in three minutes she expires.

RINALDO: Heartrending sound! Has heaven expressly formed
My soul for her alone, and will it part us?
Forever part us? We'll not part a moment:

Behold her with my eyes, ye heavens, and spare her.
URANIA: Thy prayers are all delivered to the winds.
Heaven hears not, and she dies.
RINALDO: Oh, sad reward of constancy divine!
ARMIDA: 'Tis the dread punishment of lawless love!
RINALDO: Oh, faith! Oh, matchless truth opprest by fate;
For truth itself embodied lies in thee;
And with its beauty charms the admiring world.
URANIA: 'Tis not for man to censure heaven's decrees;
As it knows how to punish, it can recompense.
By impious arts, she drew thee to her arms!
No sacred rites prepared th'unlicensed way;
For which, by heaven's severe decree, she dies
A terrible example.
But yet because her faith, her truth, her constancy
Seemed to have more than humane virtue in them,
And she expires repentant.
Heaven, that in all its sacred dispensations,
Makes the perfection of its justice shine;
A more than mortal recompense ordains for them:
For after both your mortal dates are past,
Here in this blissful region of the air,
Thou shalt forever live, with thy Armida.
ARMIDA: Nay, then you powers! You make amends for all:
These, these are sounds, which can make death delightful.
URANIA: Thus with the motion of this sacred wand,
I, in a moment drive away the mists;
That cloud your mortal eyes.
[A heavenly] scene opens, and discovers Fame [with] heroes, and heroines in the clouds.
And now behold!
If that your eyes can bear immortal splendor;
Behold where hovering on her golden wings
Bright Fame illuminates her godlike equipage.
Heroes, and heroines? In the air assembled,
A thousand glorious forms that live in pleasures
To mortals inconceivable;
With these you shall forever live;
O'er these you shall forever reign,
Forever reign united.
ARMIDA: Thou kindest, dearest, best of men, farewell?
I come, ye powers!
Rinaldo! Let no grief come near thy soul:
In insupportable delight I die.
[Armida] dies.
RINALDO: Break, heart, this very moment! Cruel powers!
Why am I such a wretch, that death avoids me?
Faith, beauty, truth, and constancy, farewell;
For a short time, farewell; farewell, ye heroes,
Who in your mansions of the air expect me.
Death, who should join me to you here, avoids me?
Then to Jerusalem I'll fly, and there
Provoke him, and compel him, to unite me
Eternally to you and my Armida.
URANIA: There I'll proclaim how he, who rules above,
Takes severe vengeance of unlawful love!
Exeunt omnes.

Finis

Epilogue

To some fine sparks methinks in yonder rows,
The brave Rinaldo, a barbarian shows.
His leaving for a camp his amorous care
Is a rude thing they'll ne'er forgive, they swear.
They ne'er could think so barb'rously, they say,
No, that young hero's mere reverse are they.
On his young cheeks Love's charming power abides,
While in his manly breast the god of war resides;
In their soft hearts, ten thousand loves have places,
But war's stern god dwells on their dreadful faces.
While the late war in all its fury raged,
They ne'er with Gauls in Belgian plains engaged:
Nor towering fame on alpine mountains sought,
But here with frightful looks, while others fought,
They guarded the weak places they had bought.
But you, who to your country and your fame,
Great souls, still sacrificed your amorous flame,
Who in each spring, the season of desire,
Left the bright dames, that set your souls on fire,
To follow William, forcing France to yield,
And hunting glory through the dusty field,
You sure with pleasure should Rinaldo view,
Who less deserves immortal fame than you.
He flew from a polluted beauty's arms,
And from the influence of malignant charms.
You from such beauty and such virtue flew,
As might enamor gods as well as you.
And you bright nymphs—
Whom for a time the noble youths forsook,
With pleasure may on lost Armida look,
Since by her weakness, your high merit shines,
And to your praise, the rudest heart inclines.
She to retain her hero in her arms,
The utmost force exerted of her charms.
You when their glory summoned yours away,
Your looks rebated and relaxed your sway,
By which you force even savages t'obey.
Your country's happiness you first designed,
To that the darlings of your souls resigned,
And sent them death, or victory, to find.
O Roman virtue! Which its trial past,
Well merits the reward it meets at last:
For since with peace the noble youths returned,
They for such worth with double fires have burned.
May lone fruition but foment the flames,
And be your loves immortal as your fames.

Additional Music from *Rinaldo and Armida*

Country Dance

Minuet

Rigadon I

Rigadon II

[D.C. Rigadon I]

Passepied I

Violin 1
Violin 2
Viola
Basso continuo
[6 5]
[♯3]
[♯3]
6
[♮5 ♯3]
[♯3]
[6]
[♮3]
[4 2]
[6]
12
[6]
[6]
[3]
[6]
[♮3]
[♮3]
19
[♯3]
[6]
[6]
[♯3]

Passepied II

[D.C. Passepied I]

Air: "Behold in what glorious condition"

Be- hold in what glo- rious con- di- tion Thou once shalt Ar- mi- da en- joy, Be-
-hold in what glo- rious con- di- tion Thou once shalt Ar- mi- da en- joy.
Fine
If mor- tal fru- i- tion be- held such a bless- ing, How much past ex-
-press- ing is such a pos- sess- ing, As nev- er dis- a- bles and nev- er can
cloy, As nev- er dis- a- bles and nev- er can cloy. Be-
D.S. al Fine

Critical Report

The Sources

Primary Sources

The primary sources for this edition are those sources most closely associated with the original production of *Rinaldo and Armida* are described below:

PS-1: John Dennis, *Rinaldo and Armida: A Tragedy* (London, 1699). This published playbook contains the complete text of the drama "as it is acted at the Theatre in Little-Lincoln's-Inn-Fields."

PS-2: John Dennis, *The Musical Entertainments in the Tragedy of Rinaldo and Armida* (London, 1699). This publication contains texts for the musical sections of the drama, along with descriptive cues and a preface in which the author discusses the relation of music and drama.

PS-3: GB-Lbl, Add. Ms. 29378. This manuscript, once owned by the nineteenth-century publisher Vincent Novello, is in large part devoted to theater works by Eccles, including not only the five musical entertainments for *Rinaldo and Armida,* but also his music for *Macbeth* (1694–95), *Europe's Revels on the Peace* (1697), and short vocal works from a number of plays.

PS-4: "Ah Queen" in John Eccles, *A Collection of Songs for One, Two, and Three Voices Together* (London, [1704]), 78. This printed anthology is the chief collection of Eccles's songs, and supplies the fifth-act aria, "Ah Queen," which is not included in PS-3.

Supplemental Sources

The following sources are used in this edition to provide music for *Rinaldo and Armida* that is not contained in the primary sources.

SS-1: John Eccles, *Theatre Musick: Being a Collection of the Newest Ayres for the Violin . . . with a Through Bass to Each Dance* (London: John Walsh, [1698]), 21–22, 25–28. This printed anthology of dances arranged for violin and unfigured bass gives dances from *Rinaldo and Armida* by Eccles, as well as airs and dances from the theatre and court by composers including Jeremiah Clarke. The collection does not indicate where in the production of *Rinaldo and Armida* the dances appeared. Their G tonality as well as the fact that the third-act chaconne also appears with the dances in the print suggests their use in the third act, but this must remain speculative.

SS-2: "Behold in what glorious condition" (London: Thomas Cross, 1699). This single sheet of music contains the attribution "A Song in the Additions to Rinaldo, set by Mr. John Eccles, Sung by Mrs. Hodgson, and exactly engraved by Thomas Cross," and the music is stylistically congruent with the rest of the opera.

Another source, GB-Lbl, Add. Ms. 17853, fols. 41v–42r, contains "No More Invade Me: A Song in the Opera of Renaldo." The style of "No more invade me" is distinctive in both its contrast to the general style of the main score and its high degree of ornamentation, and added chord tones suggest a keyboard arrangement, albeit texted. Although this manuscript associates this song with "Renaldo," several printed sources, e.g., GB-Lbl, Music Collection, shelfmarks H.1601 (313) and 303 (47), note that it was from "Hercules," a pasticcio opera (*Hercole*) with a libretto by Giacomo Rossi, performed at the Haymarket Theatre in 1712. These printed attributions as well as the stylistic contrast make the association of the song with *Rinaldo and Armida* unconvincing and tenuous. "No more invade me" also appears as the first song in a manuscript anthology of "Old English Songs" in the University of Kentucky Libraries, Special Collections, Division of Manuscripts (http://athena.uky.edu/oes/intro.htm). The heading of the manuscript folio has been trimmed in the process of binding, and thus any attribution it may have offered is irrecoverable.

Concordant Sources

Two airs ("Ah Queen" in act 5, and "The jolly breeze" in musical entertainment no. 2, mm. 170–221) and the chaconne (musical entertainment no. 4, mm. 196–274) exist in concordant sources. The sources are listed below, and significant variants are reported in the critical notes.

CS-1: Chaconne from act 3 in John Eccles, *Theatre Musick: Being a Collection of the Newest Ayres for the Violin . . . with a Through Bass to Each Dance* (London, [1698]), 23–24. The chaconne is arranged for violin and basso continuo, without figures; it omits the flute interludes and the inner parts (violin 2 and viola).

CS-2: "Ah Queen" in *Mercurius Musicus: or, The Monthly Collection of New Teaching Songs,* January [1699], 14–15. This source uses treble clef for the vocal part and lacks bass figures. Rhythms are generally simpler than in PS-4; variants that result in different melodic contours or harmonic patterns are reported in critical notes.

CS-3: "The jolly breeze" in *Twelve New Songs* (London: William Pearson, 1699), 5. This source uses treble clef for the vocal part and lacks bass figures. Other significant variants are listed in the critical notes.

CS-4: "The jolly breeze" (London: Thomas Cross, [ca. 1700]) = GB-Lbl, Music Collection, shelfmark K.7.i.2.(48). This song sheet includes the information "A Song in Rinaldo and Armida, Sung by Mr Gouge and exactly engrav'd by T. Cross" in the heading. It is otherwise identical to CS-3.

CS-5: "The jolly breeze" in John Eccles, *A Collection of Songs for One, Two, and Three Voices Together* (London, [1704]), 23. This source uses treble clef for the vocal part. Other significant variants are listed in the critical notes.

CS-6: "The jolly breeze" in *Wit and Mirth: or Pills to Purge Melancholy* (London: Playford, 1709), 160. This source give the melody only, without text underlay. The melody is identical to that of CS-3.

CS-7: "The jolly breeze" in *Collection of Choicest Songs & Dialogues* (London: Walsh, [ca. 1703–15] = GB-Lbl, Music Collection, shelfmark G.304), no. 145. This source uses treble clef for the vocal part and lacks bass figures. Other significant variants are listed in the critical notes.

CS-8: "The jolly breeze" ([London]: n.d.) = GB-Lbl, Music Collection, shelfmark H.1601 (430). This source uses treble clef for the melody and contains a figured bass. It presents the same version as CS-5 with a new heading.

Editorial Methods

This edition begins with a transcription of the prefatory materials from the printed primary sources. The spoken text of the play and the portions set to music are integrated together in this presentation. The dances and additional airs associated with the play are presented in separate sections following the play itself.

The text of the play, except those passages set to music, is taken from the playbook (PS-1); the passages set to music follow the text as given in the manuscript score (PS-3). The line numbers for the play text are editorial and include the lines set to music; the poetic presentation of the sung texts as found in PS-1, along with the corresponding line numbers within the sequence of the play as a whole, is supplied in the appendix. The stage directions applying to the speaking characters are supplied from the playbook. The descriptions of the musical numbers (whether extant or lost) are given as found in Dennis's *Musical Entertainments* (PS-2), as they provide a fuller picture of the intended stage action; the playbook cues for the musical numbers are included in the appendix. In all texts, spelling, capitalization, and punctuation has generally been tacitly corrected, regularized, and modernized. Contracted suffixes are expanded (i.e.,'d becomes *-ed*, *'n* becomes *-en*, etc.), but other contractions and archaic verb forms (especially second person singular) are retained. Abbreviations (e.g., y^e) and symbols (such as the ampersand) have been replaced by their verbal equivalents.

The musical entertainments in acts 1–4 are taken from the theater music manuscript (PS-3). This score generally lacks scoring indications; notable exceptions include the specific indication of flutes in musical entertainment no. 4 (in act 3) and the scoring for bass violins at the end of musical entertainment no. 5 (in act 4). In the main, however, scoring indications in the edition are assumed to be for string ensemble.

The edition applies tacit modernization to the following elements of notation: (1) system brackets, barlines of all types, repeat signs, and the indication of first and subsequent endings; (2) flats and sharps signifying naturals are rendered as such, both in pitch inflections and figures; (3) stem direction, and the form of rests; and (4) placement and orthography of verbal instructions within the music. The original note values are retained. Beaming has been modernized and regularized as appropriate for instrumental and vocal parts. Editorially added slurs and ties are dashed; brackets are used to signal other added elements. Editorial reconstructions (viz., violin 2 and viola parts for the dances) are presented on reduced staves.

Clefs are modernized when appropriate, namely, C3 and C4 clefs in vocal parts are transcribed in treble clef or transposing treble clef, as appropriate to range and context. The lines assigned to the viola were originally in C2 clef, but the edition uses C3 clef throughout. All other changes to the clefs are noted in the critical notes.

Key signatures have been modernized to include all accidentals needed for the prevailing key, with the original key signatures cited in the critical notes. The indication of accidentals is adapted to conform both to the modern key signatures and to the modern convention that accidentals retain their efficacy for an entire measure. Redundant accidentals are tacitly removed; editorially added accidentals are given in brackets. If an editorial accidental is followed later in the measure by an identical inflection also found in the source, both accidentals are given in the edition (with the first given in brackets).

Time signatures are modernized where necessary, as follows: 𝄵 is transcribed as $\frac{4}{4}$, ⌽ as $\frac{2}{2}$, and all archaic triple meters are transcribed as $\frac{3}{4}$. Where time signatures required modernization, the original signature appears above the staff.

Figures are given above the staff and are metrically positioned to correspond to the indicated harmonic changes. The figures have been regularized as follows: (1) thirds above the bass are indicated with a numeral, with inflections as needed; (2) the inflections are placed before the figures (e.g., ♭6, rather than 6♭); and (3) sharps and flats are presented as naturals when appropriate. Editorial additions are given in brackets. Tied notes in the continuo are combined into larger values. All extender lines indicating the continuation of a figure over a moving bass line are editorial.

Critical Notes

The critical notes report differences not covered by the editorial policy between the primary and supplemental sources and the edition. They also report the use of readings from concordant sources and list other significant variants found therein. Sources other than the primary sources are referenced by the sigla given in the description of the sources above; if no siglum is given, then the reading applies to the primary source. The critical notes also use the following abbreviations: M(m). = measure(s), S = Soprano, A= Alto, T = Tenor, B = Bass, Fl. = Flute, Vn. = Violin, Va. = Viola, B. Vn. = Bass Violin, B.c., Basso continuo. Pitch identification uses the system in which middle C = c′.

Play Text

Act 1, line 87, word 3, PS-1 gives "suppored." Act 2, line 431, word 2, PS-1 gives "least." Act 3, line 332, word 7, PS-1 gives "ir." Act 3, line 342, word 9, PS-1 gives "on." End of act 3, PS-1 gives music description as "The foresaid alarm is repeated for the act tune." Act 4, line 344, PS-1 places the stage direction at the end of line 345. Act 5, line 32, word 7, PS-1 gives "hearts."

Musical Entertainment No. 1

M. 7, B.c, note 1, figure is $^{\flat 6}_{\natural 3}$ with an upward-pointing arrow preceding it (see plate 2). M. 7, B.c., note 2, figure is $^{8}_{\flat 7}$. M. 39, Spirit, "the" underlaid at note 10. M. 48, B.c., meter is ɸ. M. 68, Vn. 2, note 4 is b♭′. M. 83, Vn. 2, Va., note 1 is dotted half (no rest following).

Musical Entertainment No. 2

M. 3, Shepherd (bass), slur begins at m. 5, note 1. M. 34, B.c., note 2 is f. M. 41, B., note 4 is f. Mm. 42–47, B, clef is G2 but pitches are written as though F4 is intended. M. 49, Vn. 2, notes 1–2 are quarter–quarter. M. 50, B.c., note 2 has figure ♯. M. 90, Shepherd (countertenor), text is "never." M. 119, Nymph, notes 1–2, text is "wishing." M. 120, Nymph, notes 1–2, text is "dying." Mm. 142, 144, S, A, T, B, notes 2–3, text is "around." M. 149, B.c., notes 1–2, figures are $^{5}_{4\,3}$. M. 162, T, note 6 is e′. M. 172, B.c. has g half–g half in CS-3, CS-5, CS-7. M. 173, B.c., beats 1–2 are d half in CS-3, CS-5, CS-7. M. 175, B.c., note 1, figures from CS-5. M. 176, B.c., beats 3–4 are A dotted quarter–G 8th in CS-3, CS-7. Mm. 177, 178, Shepherd 1, note 4 lacks ornament in CS-3, CS-5, CS-7. M. 178, B.c., note 5, figures from CS-5. M. 179, B.c., note 3 lacks figure in CS-5. M. 183, B.c., beats 3–4 are F♯ dotted quarter–F♯ 8th in CS-3, CS-5, CS-7. M. 184, B.c., beats 3–4 are e quarter–d quarter. M. 186, B.c., note 2, figure from CS-5. M. 186, B.c., beat 4 is d 8th–c 8th in CS-3, CS-5, CS-7. M. 187, B.c., note 1, figure from CS-5. M. 188, B.c., beat 4 is d 8th–c 8th in CS-5. M. 189, Shepherd 1, note 1 is e″ in CS-3 (= e′ in edition). M. 190, B.c. has G quarter–G quarter–d half in CS-5. Mm. 192–221, Nymph, clef is F4 but pitches are written as though G2 is intended.

Musical Entertainment No. 3

M. 51, Sophia, beat 3, beaming is 2 + 2, with single slur over all four notes. Mm. 151 and 158, stage directions from PS-1. M. 162, Vn. 1, notes 2–3 are f″–g″. M. 165, T, note 2 is d′.

Musical Entertainment No. 4

M. 55, B.c., note 4 has digital pointer sign. M. 57, B, notes 1–2, text is "Cupid." M. 59, S, notes 1–2, text is "come, come." M. 73, B.c., beats 1–3 are half note–quarter rest. Mm. 83 and 85, S, note 1, slur ends at note 6 of mm. 82 and 84, respectively. M. 155, Vn. 2, A, note 3 is e′. Mm. 170–73, key signature of one flat. M. 198, B.c., note 1 has ♯ (= ♮). M. 215, Va., note 1 is f′. M. 269, B.c., fig. 6 is on beat 2.

Musical Entertainment No. 5

M. 12, Vn. 2, note 4 is f′. M. 13, Va., note 6 is e′. M. 30, Va., note 3 is b♭. M. 36, Vn. 1, note 8 is lacking. M. 40, A, note 3 is a′. M. 41, B, B.c., note 9 is b♭. M. 46, Vn. 2, note 2 is a′. M. 52, Spirit, note 6, text is "quakes." M. 57, Va., note 3 is f′. M. 70, Vn. 2, Va., T, note 5 is quarter note–8th rest. M. 71, Vn. 1, notes 2–3 are slurred. M. 71, Vn. 2, Va., note 5 is quarter note–8th rest. M. 71, B, B.c., note 6 is quarter note–8th rest. M. 95, Vn. 2, note 2 is e″. M. 96, Vn. 2, note 1 is d″. M. 140, A, notes 1–2 are f′–f′. M. 141, A, note 1 is e′. M. 143, B.c., note 2, figure is $^{\sharp 4}_{3}$. M. 175, Spirit, note 1 is quarter. M. 191, Va., note 2 is f′. M. 194, Spirit, text is "thunder." M. 207, Va., note 1 is g′. M. 212, S, B, note 1 and rest are dotted quarter. M. 212, B.c., note 1, figure is $^{7}_{4}$. Mm. 213 and 214, S, notes 2–4 are slurred (see plate 2). M. 238, T has slurred e♭′ half–d′ half. M. 246, B.c., note 5 is g. M. 287, Va., note 1 is c′.

Air: "Ah Queen"

Throughout the primary source (PS-4), the vocal staff is written in G2 clef. The concordant source (CS-2) also uses G2 clef for the vocal staff, and it lacks figures. In the notes below, pitch variants are reported as though written in transposing G2 clef, as in the edition.

The meter in CS-2 is $\frac{3}{1}$ with three quarter notes in each measure (= modern $\frac{3}{4}$); thus, the note values in CS-2 are half those of PS-4. In the notes below, rhythmic variants from CS-2 are reported as though the meter is $\frac{3}{2}$, as in the edition.

M. 2, Spirit, beat 3 is e♭′ half in CS-2. M. 3, Spirit, notes 2–4 are quarter–8th–8th in CS-2. M. 3, B.c. is dotted whole in CS-2. M. 6, B.c., note 1 is d in CS-2. M. 7, B.c., beat 3 is G dotted quarter–F 8th in CS-2. M. 12, Spirit, word 2 is "cease." M. 17, Spirit, beat 2 is a♮ 8th–b♭ 8th–c′ quarter in CS-2. M. 19, Spirit, beat 2 is d′ 8th–e♭′ 8th–f′ quarter in CS-2. M. 24, Spirit, note 3 lacks flat in CS-2. Mm. 24–25, text is "and never will return" in CS-2. M. 26, B.c., note 2 is f in CS-2. M. 27, B.c., notes 1–2 are whole–half in CS-2. Mm. 27, 29, 33, 37, last word is "you." M. 35, B.c., note 3 is f in CS-2.

Country Dance

Title is "Country Dance from the Opera of Armida." Repetitions are not specified, though suggested by double barlines.

M. 12, B.c., note 4 is D.

Minuet

Repetitions are not specified, though suggested by double barlines.

Rigadon I

Title lacks number. Repetitions are not specified, though suggested by double barlines.

M. 8, Vn. 1, note 1 lacks augmentation dot. M. 24, B.c., note 1 lacks augmentation dot.

Rigadon II

Title lacks number. Repetitions are not specified, though suggested by double barlines.

M. 4, B.c., half followed by half rest.

Passepied I

Title is "paspe." Repetitions are not specified, though suggested by double barlines.

M. 6, B.c., note 2 through m. 7, note 2, illegible. M. 19, B.c., note 1 through m. 20, note 1, illegible.

Passepied II

Title is "paspe." Repetitions are not specified, though suggested by double barlines.

M. 2, B.c., note 2 is c. Mm. 5 and 10, B.c., illegible. M. 17, B.c., note 1, illegible.

Air: "Behold in what glorious condition"

M. 33, Voice, note 3 is b′.

Appendix

Playbook Versions of the Sung Texts in *Rinaldo and Armida*

Musical Entertainment No. 1

A song by the Spirits in the air. Lofty music.

SPIRIT: Ye mighty powers who rule the air,
Ye gods who in the ocean dwell,
And ye who at the center govern hell,
Hither at great Armida's call repair;
And while by your command these towers arise,
Till with unequaled pomp and state,
Their soaring heads salute the skies,
Show those above that hell can too create.

Musical Entertainment No. 2

Spirits in the shapes of shepherds and nymphs.

SHEPHERD: Welcome to these lovely plains,
The happy seats of blissful swains.
NYMPH: Welcome to these blissful shades,
The soft retreats of happy maids.
SHEPHERDS: Here we feel no want nor care,
And no inclemency of air,
And lovers never here despair.
SHEPHERD: Sorrow ever from us flies,
Pleasure revels in our eyes.
If we pass an hour in courting,
'Tis for more delicious sporting,
Never cruel nymph denies.
NYMPH: If anything like sorrow's seen
In our voice, or in our mien,
'Tis not grief that gives the anguish,
'Tis with pleasure that we languish;
And if ever nymph denies,
'Tis like one in love who's wise;
'Tis like one who would invite
To more delicate delight,
'Tis with wishing, dying eyes.
CHORUS: All about us and above,
Gaiety and love inspires;
All about us and above
Infuses tenderness and love,
And wanton fine desires.
SHEPHERD: The jolly breeze
That comes whistling through the trees,
From all the blissful region brings
Perfumes upon its spicy wings,
With its wanton motion curling.
The crystal rills,
Which down the hills
Run o'er golden gravel purling.
NYMPH: All around venereal turtles
Cooing, billing, on the myrtles;
The more they show their amorous trouble,
More fiercely dart their piercing kisses,
And more eagerly redouble
The raptures of their murmuring blisses.

Musical Entertainment No. 3

Spirits or Dreams arise in the shapes of Bertoldo and Sophia, parents to Rinaldo; and of some that Rinaldo had slain in battle.

BERTOLDO: Rinaldo!
SOPHIA: Rinaldo!
BERTOLDO: Look up, behold the mournful shade
Of him who gave thee breath,
Who steps to see thee, while thou'rt laid
Upon the confines here of death;
T'inform thee of thy future state,
And ere yet it be too late,
To prevent thy wretched fate.
SOPHIA: Look up, my son, look upon me,
In me th'afflicted Sophia see.
Ah, son! Not all the grinding throes,
With which, when thou wert born,
My tortured nerves were torn,
Equaled half the wracking woes,
Which now thy mother undergoes,
Thou darling of my soul, for thee.
BERTOLDO: Last night I cast a look
Upon fate's dreadful book,
And read a lesson which no brain
That is mortal can sustain,
While all my soul with horror shook.
SOPHIA: Oh, the distraction of the sight!
And oh, the torments of the fright!
I never, never shall forget that night.
BERTOLDO: Rouse all thy faculties, my son,
And to my fatal words give ear,
For know that they concern thee near;
No longer let thy fancy run
After that airy phantom Fame;
But love Armida with a constant flame:
Or destiny decrees,
Thou shalt feel woes, which but to hear
Would distract thy soul with fear,
And all thy blood with horror freeze.
SOPHIA: Ah! See around the raving hosts
Of purple ghosts
Whose blood thou hast in battle spilt
With fearful guilt,
Who, unless awed by her commanding power,
Would, ah, this moment tear thee and devour!
BERTOLDO: How they advance with whirling brands,
Dance begins.
All flaming in their threatening hands!
And as they go their dreadful round,
Revenge, revenge resound!
CHORUS OF SPIRITS: For revenge, for revenge, to Armida we call,
That we terribly may on our murderer fall;
That as now we with sulphurous torches surround him,

We with our screams and our scorpions may wound him;
And with astonishing horrors confound him.
During the chorus a dance of spirits.

Musical Entertainment No. 4

[A] symphony of flutes [is played].
[Enter] Venus, Cupid, and a chorus of Loves and Graces.
VENUS: Cupid, come to the relief
Of thy mother's piercing grief;
Hither quickly, Cupid, fly;
With thee bring thy keenest dart,
To subdue a rebel heart,
Thou art scorned as well as I.
[A] ritornelle [is played].
CHORUS: Come Cupid, on thy golden wing,
And in thy sounding quiver bring
Pernicious arrows winged with fire,
T'inflict incurable desire.
[A] symphony [is played].
CUPID: *(flying down)* Thus flying through the balmy air,
To my great parent I repair;
And though the world's maintained by me,
Yet, Mother, to attend on thee,
I leave the mighty care.
VENUS: A mortal in this fragrant bower,
Presumes that he's above our power.
CUPID: I'll make that mortal know,
That none too great for Love can grow;
I tame the mighty powers above,
And cruel gods below.
[A] ritornelle [is played].
Great Jove, whose arms the lightning fling,[1]
Has felt my[2] fiercer fire,
And hell's inexorable king
Has yielded to desire.
CHORUS: Great Jove, whose arms the lightning fling,
Has felt thy fiercer fire, etc.
CUPID: Now quickly through th'enchanted grove,[3]
Let all my nimble brethren rove.
Dance
VENUS: Let earth, and air, and flood, and fire,
And everything around conspire
To breathe forth soft and sweet desire.
CHORUS: Let earth, and air, etc.

Musical Entertainment No. 5

Thunder and lightning. Spirit comes forward and sings.
SPIRIT: Ye spirits that dwell in earth, fire, and air,
Hither, hither, hither, hither, hurrying repair;
Behold your great mistress, Armida's betrayed,
Hither, hither, hither, hurry all to her aid.
CHORUS: Lo, from earth, from hell, and from sky,
With vengeance laden we fly.
SPIRIT: Ye fiends that are lurking in graves,
Or gliding in vaulted caves,
All working amain in your holes,
Heave up the crumbling earth like moles,
Till the mountain shakes,
And the rock its basis forsakes,[4]
And the heart of the traitor quakes.
CHORUS: 'Tis done, see the mountain shakes,
And the rock its basis forsakes.[5]
SPIRIT: Ye powers who govern the air,
Let nought but confusion be there;
Haste to send forth
The stormy north,
And unbind the deep mouth
Of the blustering south:
Let them blow, let them blow, till with fury they roar,
And ambitious old Ocean disdains the shore.
CHORUS: Hark how they blow! Hark how they blow!
If they go on, through the void they will sweep
The heavens, the earth, and the deep,
And the world into chaos will throw!
SPIRIT: Now flying in crowds,
Charge, charge all your clouds,
Charge them all with destructive thunder,
Let it roar till it rents the vast all asunder.
Let the lightning fearfully blaze,
Till mortals who gaze,
Fall dead at the terrible wonder.
CHORUS: 'Tis done, 'tis done, and we shake
At the dire confusion we make.
SPIRIT: Ye furies who reign in unquenchable fires,
To the sound of your yells tune your horrible lyres;
And give us that music by which you redouble
The horrors of hell and unspeakable trouble.
CHORUS: 'Tis done.
SPIRIT: Now add to the symphony clinking of chains.
CHORUS OF SPIRITS: 'Tis done.
SPIRIT: Add the howls of the damned, in the height of their pains.
CHORUS: 'Tis done.
SPIRIT: Add their screams and their roar, and their serpentine hiss.
CHORUS: 'Tis done.
SPIRIT: Let Lucifer's thunder now answer to this,
And bellow alternately through the abyss.
CHORUS: 'Tis done, and 'tis past our power to know,
Whither this be Chaos or no?

Air: "Ah Queen"

SPIRIT: Ah Queen! Ah wretched Queen give o'er,
Cease, cease with hopeless fire[6] to burn,
Ah, cease his absence to deplore:
Who now, even now forsakes the shore,
And never, never will return,
No never see thee more.

Notes

1. PS-2 has "flung."
2. PS-3 has "thy."
3. PS-3 includes two additional lines for Cupid before line 115: "But let us cease our soaring strains, / Love conquers most when he complains."
4. PS-3 does not set line 41.
5. PS-3 sets the line "And the heart of the traitor quakes."
6. PS-2 and PS-4 have "fires."

Recent Researches in the Music of the Baroque Era
Steven Saunders, general editor

Vol.	*Composer: Title*
1	Marc-Antoine Charpentier: *Judicium Salomonis*
2	Georg Philipp Telemann: *Forty-eight Chorale Preludes*
3	Johann Caspar Kerll: *Missa Superba*
4–5	Jean-Marie Leclair: *Sonatas for Violin and Basso continuo, Opus 5*
6	*Ten Eighteenth-Century Voluntaries*
7–8	William Boyce: *Two Anthems for the Georgian Court*
9	Giulio Caccini: *Le nuove musiche*
10–11	Jean-Marie Leclair: *Sonatas for Violin and Basso continuo, Opus 9 and Opus 15*
12	Johann Ernst Eberlin: *Te Deum; Dixit Dominus; Magnificat*
13	Gregor Aichinger: *Cantiones Ecclesiasticae*
14–15	Giovanni Legrenzi: *Cantatas and Canzonets for Solo Voice*
16	Giovanni Francesco Anerio and Francesco Soriano: *Two Settings of Palestrina's "Missa Papae Marcelli"*
17	Giovanni Paolo Colonna: *Messe a nove voci concertata con stromenti*
18	Michel Corrette: *"Premier livre d'orgue" and "Nouveau livre de noëls"*
19	Maurice Greene: *Voluntaries and Suites for Organ and Harpsichord*
20	Giovanni Antonio Piani: *Sonatas for Violin Solo and Violoncello with Cembalo*
21–22	Marin Marais: *Six Suites for Viol and Thoroughbass*
23–24	Dario Castello: *Selected Ensemble Sonatas*
25	*A Neapolitan Festa a Ballo and Selected Instrumental Ensemble Pieces*
26	Antonio Vivaldi: *The Manchester Violin Sonatas*
27	Louis-Nicolas Clérambault: *Two Cantatas for Soprano and Chamber Ensemble*
28	Giulio Caccini: *Nuove musiche e nuova maniera di scriverle (1614)*
29–30	Michel Pignolet de Montéclair: *Cantatas for One and Two Voices*
31	Tomaso Albinoni: *Twelve Cantatas, Opus 4*
32–33	Antonio Vivaldi: *Cantatas for Solo Voice*
34	Johann Kuhnau: *Magnificat*
35	Johann Stadlmayr: *Selected Magnificats*
36–37	Jacopo Peri: *Euridice: An Opera in One Act, Five Scenes*
38	Francesco Severi: *Salmi passaggiati (1615)*
39	George Frideric Handel: *Six Concertos for the Harpsichord or Organ (Walsh's Transcriptions, 1738)*
40	*The Brasov Tablature (Brasov Music Manuscript 808): German Keyboard Studies 1608–1684*
41	John Coprario: *Twelve Fantasias for Two Bass Viols and Organ and Eleven Pieces for Three Lyra Viols*

42 Antonio Cesti: *Il pomo d'oro (Music for Acts III and V from Modena, Biblioteca Estense, Ms. Mus. E. 120)*
43 Tomaso Albinoni: *Pimpinone: Intermezzi comici musicali*
44–45 Antonio Lotti: *Duetti, terzetti, e madrigali a piu voci*
46 Matthias Weckmann: *Four Sacred Concertos*
47 Jean Gilles: *Requiem (Messe des morts)*
48 Marc-Antoine Charpentier: *Vocal Chamber Music*
49 *Spanish Art Song in the Seventeenth Century*
50 Jacopo Peri: *"Le varie musiche" and Other Songs*
51–52 Tomaso Albinoni: *Sonatas and Suites, Opus 8, for Two Violins, Violoncello, and Basso continuo*
53 Agostino Steffani: *Twelve Chamber Duets*
54–55 Gregor Aichinger: *The Vocal Concertos*
56 Giovanni Battista Draghi: *Harpsichord Music*
57 *Concerted Sacred Music of the Bologna School*
58 Jean-Marie Leclair: *Sonatas for Violin and Basso continuo, Opus 2*
59 Isabella Leonarda: *Selected Compositions*
60–61 Johann Schelle: *Six Chorale Cantatas*
62 Denis Gaultier: *La Rhétorique des Dieux*
63 Marc-Antoine Charpentier: *Music for Molière's Comedies*
64–65 Georg Philipp Telemann: *Don Quichotte auf der Hochzeit des Comacho: Comic Opera-Serenata in One Act*
66 Henry Butler: *Collected Works*
67–68 John Jenkins: *The Lyra Viol Consorts*
69 *Keyboard Transcriptions from the Bach Circle*
70 Melchior Franck: *Geistliche Gesäng und Melodeyen*
71 Georg Philipp Telemann: *Douze solos, à violon ou traversière*
72 Marc-Antoine Charpentier: *Nine Settings of the "Litanies de la Vierge"*
73 *The Motets of Jacob Praetorius II*
74 Giovanni Porta: *Selected Sacred Music from the Ospedale della Pietà*
75 *Fourteen Motets from the Court of Ferdinand II of Hapsburg*
76 Jean-Marie Leclair: *Sonatas for Violin and Basso continuo, Opus 1*
77 Antonio Bononcini: *Complete Sonatas for Violoncello and Basso continuo*
78 Christoph Graupner: *Concerti Grossi for Two Violins*
79 Paolo Quagliati: *Il primo libro de' madrigali a quattro voci*
80 Melchior Franck: *Dulces Mundani Exilij Deliciae*
81 *Late-Seventeenth-Century English Keyboard Music*
82 *Solo Compositions for Violin and Viola da gamba with Basso continuo*
83 Barbara Strozzi: *Cantate, ariete a una, due e tre voci, Opus 3*
84 Charles-Hubert Gervais: *Super flumina Babilonis*
85 Henry Aldrich: *Selected Anthems and Motet Recompositions*

86 Lodovico Grossi da Viadana: *Salmi a quattro cori*
87 Chiara Margarita Cozzolani: *Motets*
88 Elisabeth-Claude Jacquet de La Guerre: *Cephale et Procris*
89 Sébastien Le Camus: *Airs à deux et trois parties*
90 Thomas Ford: *Lyra Viol Duets*
91 *Dedication Service for St. Gertrude's Chapel, Hamburg, 1607*
92 Johann Klemm: *Partitura seu Tabulatura italica*
93 Giovanni Battista Somis: *Sonatas for Violin and Basso continuo, Opus 3*
94 John Weldon: *The Judgment of Paris*
95–96 Juan Bautista Comes: *Masses. Parts 1–2*
97 Sebastian Knüpfer: *Lustige Madrigalien und Canzonetten*
98 Stefano Landi: *La morte d'Orfeo*
99 Giovanni Battista Fontana: *Sonatas for One, Two, and Three Parts with Basso continuo*
100 Georg Philipp Telemann: *Twelve Trios*
101 Fortunato Chelleri: *Keyboard Music*
102 Johann David Heinichen: *La gara degli Dei*
103 Johann David Heinichen: *Diana su l'Elba*
104 Alessandro Scarlatti: *Venere, Amore e Ragione*
105 *Songs with Theorbo (ca. 1650–1663)*
106 Melchior Franck: *Paradisus Musicus*
107 Heinrich Ignaz Franz von Biber: *Missa Christi resurgentis*
108 Johann Ludwig Bach: *Motets*
109–10 Giovanni Rovetta: *Messa, e salmi concertati, op. 4 (1639). Parts 1–2*
111 Johann Joachim Quantz: *Seven Trio Sonatas*
112 Petits motets *from the Royal Convent School at Saint-Cyr*
113 Isabella Leonarda: *Twelve Sonatas, Opus 16*
114 Rudolph di Lasso: *Virginalia Eucharistica (1615)*
115 Giuseppe Torelli: *Concerti musicali, Opus 6*
116–17 Nicola Francesco Haym: *Complete Sonatas. Parts 1–2*
118 Benedetto Marcello: *Il pianto e il riso delle quattro stagioni*
119 Loreto Vittori: *La Galatea*
120–23 William Lawes: *Collected Vocal Music. Parts 1–4*
124 Marco da Gagliano: *Madrigals. Part 1*
125 Johann Schop: *Erster Theil newer Paduanen*
126 Giovanni Felice Sances: *Motetti a una, due, tre, e quattro voci (1638)*
127 Thomas Elsbeth: *Sontägliche Evangelien*
128–30 Giovanni Antonio Rigatti: *Messa e salmi, parte concertati. Parts 1–3*
131 *Seventeenth-Century Lutheran Church Music with Trombones*
132 Francesco Cavalli: *La Doriclea*
133 *Music for "Macbeth"*

134	Domenico Allegri: *Music for an Academic Defense (Rome, 1617)*
135	Jean Gilles: *Diligam te, Domine*
136	Silvius Leopold Weiss: *Lute Concerti*
137	*Masses by Alessandro Scarlatti and Francesco Gasparini*
138	Giovanni Ghizzolo: *Madrigali et arie per sonare et cantare*
139	Michel Lambert: *Airs from "Airs de différents autheurs"*
140	William Babell: *Twelve Solos for a Violin or Oboe with Basso Continuo. Book 1*
141	Giovanni Francesco Anerio: *Selva armonica (Rome, 1617)*
142–43	Bellerofonte Castaldi: *Capricci (1622). Parts 1–2*
144	Georg von Bertouch: *Sonatas a 3*
145	Marco da Gagliano: *Madrigals. Part 2*
146	Giovanni Rovetta: *Masses*
147	Giacomo Antonio Perti: *Five-Voice Motets for the Assumption of the Virgin Mary*
148	Giovanni Felice Sances: *Motetti a 2, 3, 4, e cinque voci (1642)*
149	*La grand-mére amoureuse, parodie d'Atys*
150	Andreas Hammerschmidt: *Geistlicher Dialogen Ander Theil*
151	Georg von Bertouch: *Three Sacred Cantatas*
152	Giovanni Maria Ruggieri: *Two Settings of the Gloria*
153	Alessandro Scarlatti: *Concerti sacri, opera seconda*
154	Johann Sigismund Kusser: *Adonis*
155	John Blow: *Selected Verse Anthems*
156	Anton Holzner: *Viretum pierium (1621)*
157	Alessandro Scarlatti: *Venere, Adone, et Amore*
158	Marc-Antoine Charpentier: *In nativitatem Domini canticum, H. 416*
159	Francesco Scarlatti: *Six Concerti Grossi*
160	Charles Avison: *Concerto Grosso Arrangements of Geminiani's Opus 1 Violin Sonatas*
161	Johann David Heinichen: *Selected Music for Vespers*
162–63	Francesco Gasparini: *Cantatas with Violins. Parts 1–2*
164–65	Antoine Boesset: *Sacred Music. Parts 1–2*
166	Andreas Hammerschmidt: *Selections from the "Gespräche" (1655–56) with Capellen*
167	Santiago de Murcia: *Cifras selectas de guitarra*
168	Gottfried Heinrich Stölzel: *German Te Deum*
169	Biagio Marini: *Compositioni varie per musica di camera, Opus 13*
170	Santiago Billoni: *Complete Works*
171	Marco da Gagliano: *La Flora*
172	Girolamo Polani: *Six Chamber Cantatas for Solo Voice*
173	Bonifazio Graziani: *Motets for Two to Six Voices, Opus 1*
174	Marco da Gagliano: *Madrigals. Part 3*
175	Alessandro Scarlatti: *Solo Serenatas*
176	John Eccles: *Rinaldo and Armida*